WISCONSIN ROCKS!

A Guide to Geologic Sites in the Badger State

SCOTT SPOOLMAN

2018
Mountain Press Publishing Company
Missoula, Montana

Photos by author unless otherwise credited.
Maps constructed by Chelsea Feeney (www.cmcfeeney.com).
Cover photo: Banded gneiss at Big Falls County Park east of Eau Claire.
Back cover photo: Stand Rock, a pedestal of sandstone in the Dells of the Wisconsin River.

GEOLOGY ROCKS!

A state-by-state series that introduces readers to some of the most compelling and accessible geologic sites in each state.

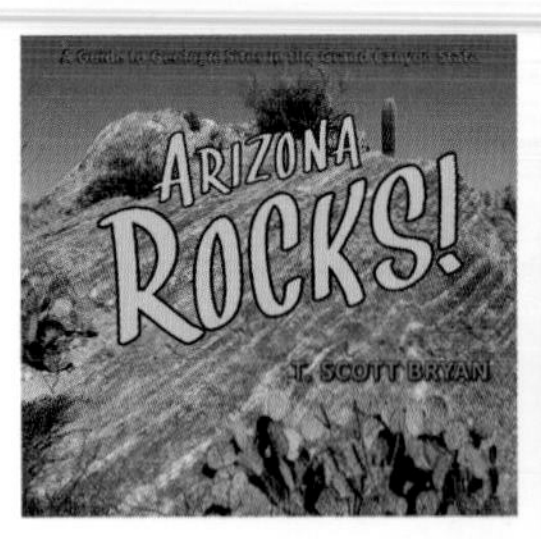

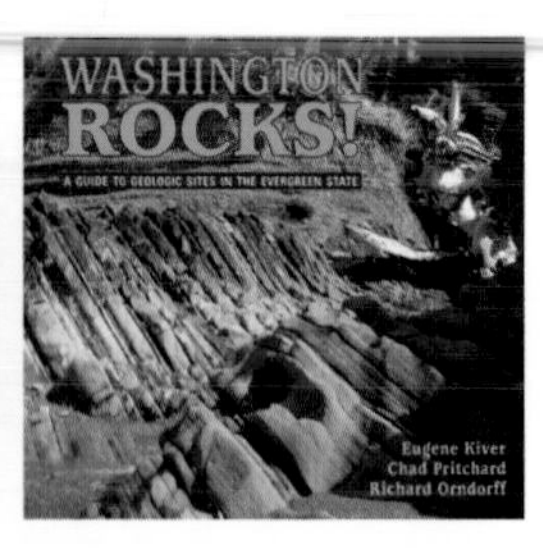

Library of Congress Cataloging-in-Publication Data

Names: Spoolman, Scott, author.
Title: Wisconsin rocks! : a guide to geologic sites in the Badger State / Scott Spoolman.
Description: Missoula, Montana : Mountain Press Publishing Company, 2018. | Includes bibliographical references and index.
Identifiers: LCCN 2018024066 | ISBN 9780878426898 (pbk. : alk. paper)
Subjects: LCSH: Geology—Wisconsin—Guidebooks. | Wisconsin—Guidebooks.
Classification: LCC QE179 .S66 2018 | DDC 557.775—dc23
LC record available at https://lccn.loc.gov/2018024066

PRINTED IN THE UNITED STATES

P.O. Box 2399 • Missoula, MT 59806 • 406-728-1900
800-234-5308 • info@mtnpress.com
www.mountain-press.com

For Gail, whose love of learning inspires me.

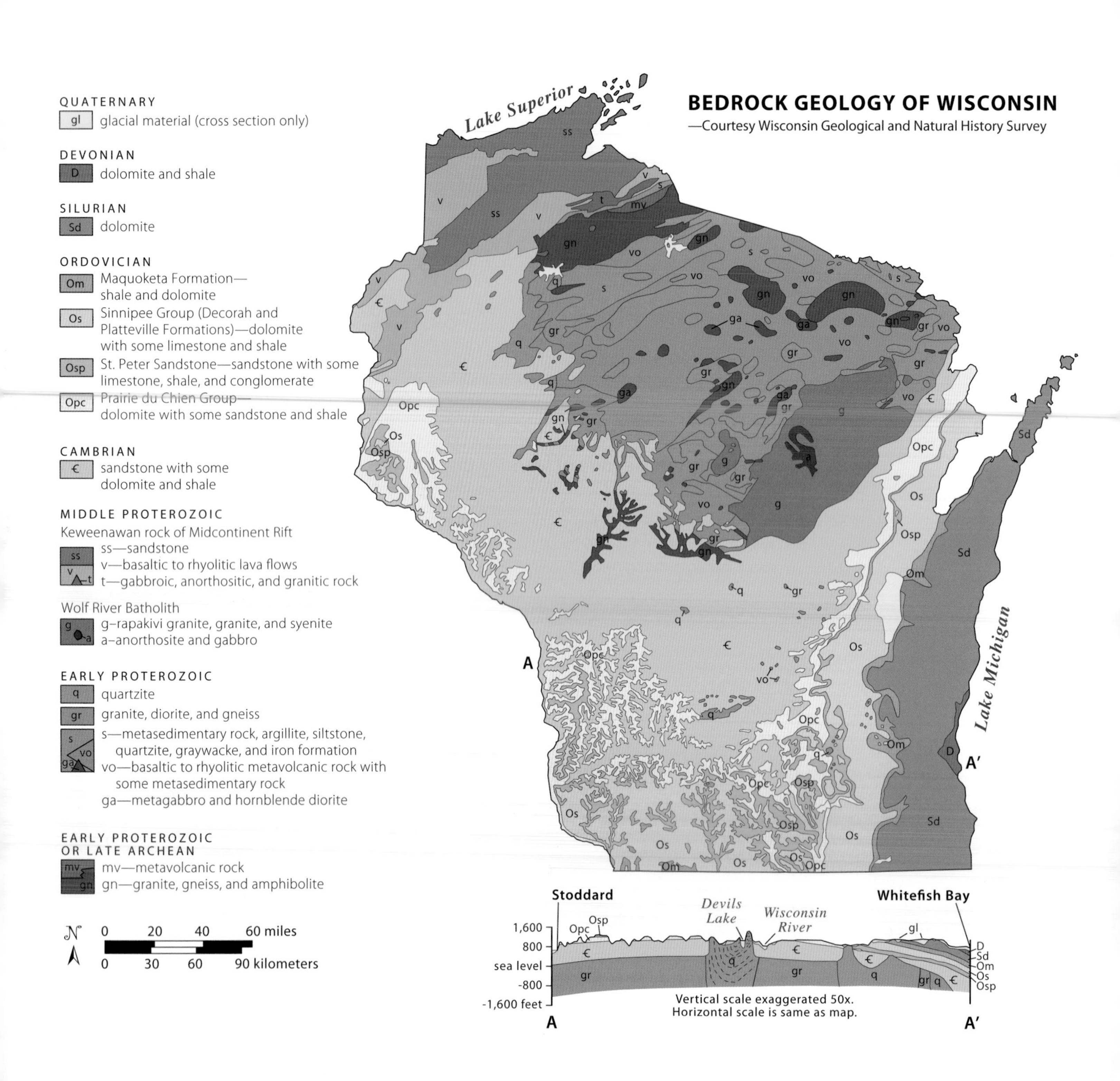
BEDROCK GEOLOGY OF WISCONSIN
—Courtesy Wisconsin Geological and Natural History Survey
QUATERNARY
gl glacial material (cross section only)
DEVONIAN
D dolomite and shale
SILURIAN
Sd dolomite
ORDOVICIAN
Om Maquoketa Formation—shale and dolomite
Os Sinnipee Group (Decorah and Platteville Formations)—dolomite with some limestone and shale
Osp St. Peter Sandstone—sandstone with some limestone, shale, and conglomerate
Opc Prairie du Chien Group—dolomite with some sandstone and shale
CAMBRIAN
€ sandstone with some dolomite and shale
MIDDLE PROTEROZOIC
Keweenawan rock of Midcontinent Rift
ss—sandstone
v—basaltic to rhyolitic lava flows
t—gabbroic, anorthositic, and granitic rock
Wolf River Batholith
g–rapakivi granite, granite, and syenite
a–anorthosite and gabbro
EARLY PROTEROZOIC
q quartzite
gr granite, diorite, and gneiss
s—metasedimentary rock, argillite, siltstone, quartzite, graywacke, and iron formation
vo—basaltic to rhyolitic metavolcanic rock with some metasedimentary rock
ga—metagabbro and hornblende diorite
EARLY PROTEROZOIC OR LATE ARCHEAN
mv—metavolcanic rock
gn—granite, gneiss, and amphibolite
0 20 40 60 miles
0 30 60 90 kilometers
Lake Superior
Lake Michigan
A
A'
Stoddard
Devils Lake
Wisconsin River
Whitefish Bay
1,600
800
sea level
-800
-1,600 feet
Vertical scale exaggerated 50x.
Horizontal scale is same as map.

PREFACE

Wisconsin's surprisingly varied landscapes are the result of a long and complex geologic story that includes mountain-building continental collisions, intensive volcanic activity, a great rift in the Earth's crust, shallow seas teeming with primitive life, and centuries of crushing glacial activity.

Tucked into a corner of the Upper Midwest the state boasts two inland coasts—those of Lakes Superior and Michigan. The mighty Mississippi River, miles wide in some places, forms a third shoreline, while the wide Wisconsin River bisects the state from northeast to southwest. Many stretches of these shorelines and riverbanks are lined with imposing sandstone bluffs that are dressed in shades of green and pink in springtime and in brilliant reds, oranges, and yellows in the fall. The north-central part of Wisconsin displays exposures of Precambrian rock on the southern edge of the Canadian Shield—the core of ancient North America. Eastern Wisconsin shows off the Niagara Escarpment, that great ridge of Silurian dolomite that arcs northeast to southeast around the basin of Lakes Michigan and Huron to where it forms the ledge over which crashes its namesake, Niagara Falls.

The state's vast ranges of hummocks, kettles, kames, drumlins, eskers, and outwash plains are world-class showcases for the handiwork of glaciers. And the unique southwestern corner of Wisconsin preserves hundreds of millions of years of uninterrupted stream erosion, etched in an arterial pattern across the unglaciated Driftless Area—famous for its deep hollows, high ridges, and picturesque sandstone crags, buttes, and pinnacles. Straddling the line between glaciated and unglaciated land, the Baraboo Hills stand as they have through 1.7 billion years of erosion, showing off their masses of purple quartzite.

Each of these regions of Wisconsin contains dozens of fascinating geological features. Most can be reached easily by driving or hiking on designated trails. Some of those trails require hiking on somewhat challenging terrain, and sturdy hiking boots are always a good idea. A few sites are on private land and available for viewing only. Most of the sites are preserved within Wisconsin's more than 100 state parks, state forests, and state recreation areas, and more than 650 state natural areas, as well as in hundreds of county and municipal parks. And some sites lie along the Ice Age National Scenic Trail, a set of trail segments that traces the outermost margin of the most recent glacier. Enjoy this sampling of Wisconsin's geologic legacy.

Gibraltar Rock with Wisconsin River valley in distance.

ACKNOWLEDGMENTS

Researching and writing this book was a challenging and greatly enjoyable experience, and many people helped me along the way. I first want to thank my editor at Mountain Press Publishing, Jennifer Carey, for giving me the opportunity to write the book, as well as for her generous and patient support throughout the process. Special thanks go also to Bethany Brander of Pendarvis Historic Site, Mark Crawford, Marie Dvorzak of the University of Wisconsin–Madison Geology Library, Tom Fitz of Northland College, John Luczaj of University Wisconsin–Green Bay, Carol McCartney of the Wisconsin Geological and Natural History Survey, and Richard Slaughter of the UW–Madison Geology Museum, for their valuable technical advice and reviews of parts of the manuscript.

Many others, including professional geologists, workers associated with the sites, and knowledgeable friends, made the job easier for me by providing good ideas, information, and support. They include Jason Anderson, Kim Anderson, and Annaka Clement of Cave of the Mounds; Bruce Brown, Linda Deith, Brad Gottschalk, Steve Mauel, and Jill Pongetti of the Wisconsin Geological and Natural History Survey; Michael Day of UW–Milwaukee; Kurt and Hanneke DeLap; the late Robert H. Dott Jr. of UW–Madison; Steven Dutch of UW–Green Bay; Kasey Fiske and Al Schema of the Wisconsin Speleological Society; Rod Gont of the Chippewa Moraine State Recreation Area; Bob Hagen; John Helling of the Ice Age Trail Alliance; Mary Huck and Jenny Smith of Bevans Lead Mine; Rosie Meinholz; Jane Mingari of the Ledge View Nature Center; Keith Montgomery of UW–Marathon County; Tom Podlesney; Jon Robaidek of the Wisconsin Department of Natural Resources; Bobbi Rongstad; and George Rothdrake.

In addition, several people provided photos to supplement or improve on my own. Thanks go to Jason Anderson, Jeff Bach, Joy Gieseke, John Luczaj, and Al Schema for these excellent photographs.

Heartfelt thanks go to my parents, Arthur and Betty Spoolman, for sparking my fascination about Wisconsin's natural beauty; my brothers, John and Rick, and sister, Amy, for their moral support and good humor; and my children, Will and Katie, for help with photographs and computer challenges.

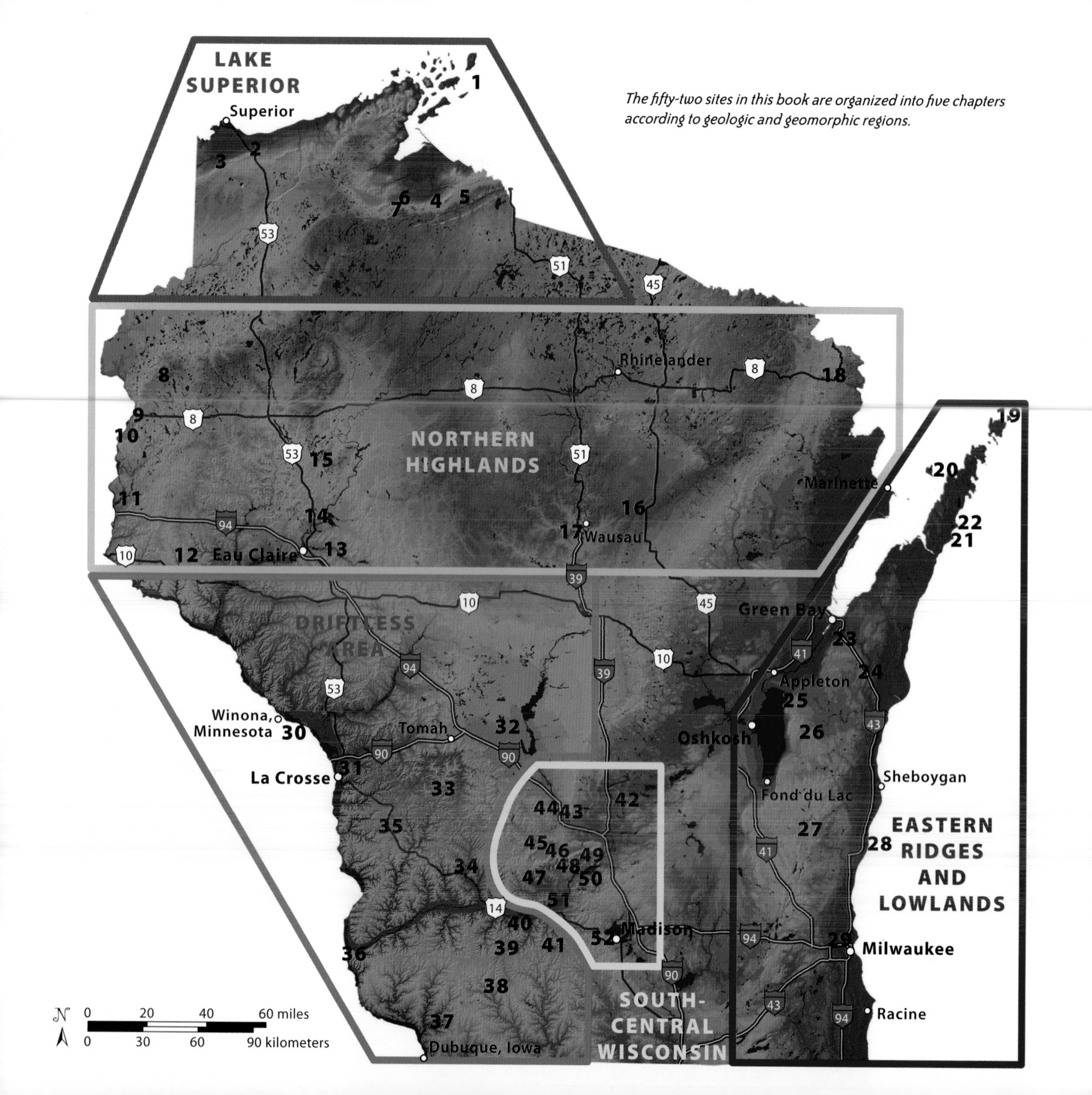

The fifty-two sites in this book are organized into five chapters according to geologic and geomorphic regions.

CONTENTS

GEOLOGIC TIME SCALE

Era	Period	Epoch	Age	Important Geologic Events in Wisconsin
CENOZOIC	Quaternary	Holocene	0.01	Last glacier departs.
		Pleistocene	**2.6**	Glaciers shape the land; Driftless Area remains untouched by ice.
	Tertiary (Neogene)	Pliocene	5.3	
		Miocene	23.0	Wisconsin moves into present location by 10 million years ago.
	Tertiary (Paleogene)	Oligocene	33.9	
		Eocene	56.0	
		Paleocene	**66.0**	
MESOZOIC	Cretaceous		145	Long period of erosion leaves no rock record from 400 to 2 million years ago.
	Jurassic		201	
	Triassic		**252**	
PALEOZOIC	Permian		299	
	Carboniferous	Pennsylvanian	323	
		Mississippian	359	
	Devonian		419	
	Silurian		444	Dolomite of Niagara Escarpment is deposited.
	Ordovician		485	Paleozoic seas advance and retreat, depositing many layers of sedimentary rock.
	Cambrian		**541**	Wisconsin is south of equator, moving north.
PRECAMBRIAN	Proterozoic Eon	Neoproterozoic	1,000	Douglas Fault forms 900 to 500 million years ago. Wisconsin Dome forms between 1,109 and 1,000 million years ago. Midcontinent Rift forms 1,100 million years ago.
		Mesoproterozoic	1,600	Wolf River Batholith forms 1,500 million years ago.
		Paleoproterozoic	2,500	Sandstone deposited that will one day be Baraboo Hills and Rib Mountain. Volcanoes erupt in south 1,760 million years ago. Penokean Mountains form 1,850 million years ago from collision of Superior and Marshfield cratons.
	Archean Eon		3,850	Oldest rocks in Wisconsin form.
	Hadean Eon		**4,600**	Approximate age of Earth.

age in millions of years before present

WISCONSIN'S LANDSCAPES

The geologic story of Wisconsin's landscapes starts more than 3 billion years ago. That's 3,000 million years ago! Wisconsin's oldest rock is 2,700-million-year-old gneiss, a coarse-grained metamorphic rock. Found in the north-central part of the state, this old bedrock, part of a mass of ancient bedrock known as the Canadian Shield, was once a small continent that, through amalgamation with other small continents, eventually became North America. The crystalline rocks of the shield underlie most of central and eastern Canada and parts of Minnesota, Wisconsin, and New York. The shield is a complex mosaic of varying types of rock with a long history that's difficult to decipher. Among the intrusive igneous rock types, a particularly beautiful and durable type of granite of varying shades of gray, pink, and red is Wisconsin's official state rock. Known as ruby red granite, it outcrops in Wisconsin's central and northeastern counties.

Wisconsin's state rock, red granite.

The varying landscapes we see today in Wisconsin really began to take shape about 1,900 million years ago. The ancient continent lay just south of the equator back then. Because of the shifting of Earth's crustal plates atop the underlying hot, plastic mantle, the plate on which Wisconsin rides slowly traveled inch by inch, year by year, to its present location halfway between the equator and the north pole. The area of land that would become Wisconsin was oriented east and west and eventually rotated to its north-south orientation as it moved from the tropics to its present-day temperate location.

The primitive North American continent was a barren land of rock and sand 1,900 million years ago, a tropical desert not unlike the Sahara of today. It would remain lifeless for many hundreds of millions of years. What would become far northern Wisconsin and the Upper Peninsula of Michigan were on the south shore of what geologists call the Superior continent. To the south, across a shallow sea, was the smaller Marshfield continent.

Beginning about 1,900 million years ago, tectonic forces drove the two crustal plates bearing these continents straight toward each other, and during the next 115 million years, they collided. As they met, the southern edge of the northern plate was driven under the southern plate in a process called *subduction*. When this happens, the leading edge of the subducting, or diving, plate gets mangled, with some of its rock sinking into the mantle, where it melts and creates new magma, or molten rock. This magma can then rise through the crust along fractures, erupting on the surface to build volcanoes. A string of volcanoes, similar to the present-day island chain that includes Japan, was created in the narrowing sea between the Superior and Marshfield continents. As the plates continued colliding, the Superior continent eventually acquired the chain of volcanoes, making them part of its southern shore, and the Superior and Marshfield continents finally joined together in a colossal fusion of landmasses.

The collision generated a mountain range, called the Penokean Mountains, across parts of present-day Minnesota, northern Wisconsin, the Upper Peninsula of Michigan, and southern Ontario. Their footprint was something like that of the Appalachian Mountains of today. No one knows how high they rose, but had they not been continually eroding, their highest peaks might have risen higher than today's Rocky Mountains. However, they did not at all resemble today's mountains. Land plants had not yet evolved, so the Penokean peaks were barren and rocky, and the tropical climate subjected them to intense erosion by wind and rain.

About 1,760 million years ago, the region south of the Penokeans experienced a period of volcanic activity. Intrusions of magma created massive underground bodies of granite, a light-colored, coarse-grained rock composed primarily of quartz and potassium feldspar. Violent eruptions covered much of the land surface with volcanic ash and rhyolite, a reddish, fine-grained volcanic rock with the same minerals as granite. When the volcanic activity ended, a shallow sea invaded the area from the south. Streams carried sand and mud southward to the seashore from the eroding Penokean Mountains and from volcanic peaks. The sea eventually covered all of Wisconsin, and after millions of years the seafloor was covered deeply by these sediments. With time, pressure, and certain chemical reactions, the sand and mud became layers of sandstone and shale hundreds to thousands of feet thick.

Sometime around 1,700 to 1,630 million years ago, another continental collision heaved up a mountain range near the southern shore of the continent, then located in northern Illinois. The thick layers of sandstone were mashed and folded and converted to quartzite, a very hard metamorphic rock. These mountains were not as high or extensive as the Penokeans, but much of their quartzite, one of the hardest types of rock on the planet, has resisted erosion to this day. Remnants of this range make up the Baraboo Hills as well as other prominent peaks in Wisconsin. Another major movement of magma occurred

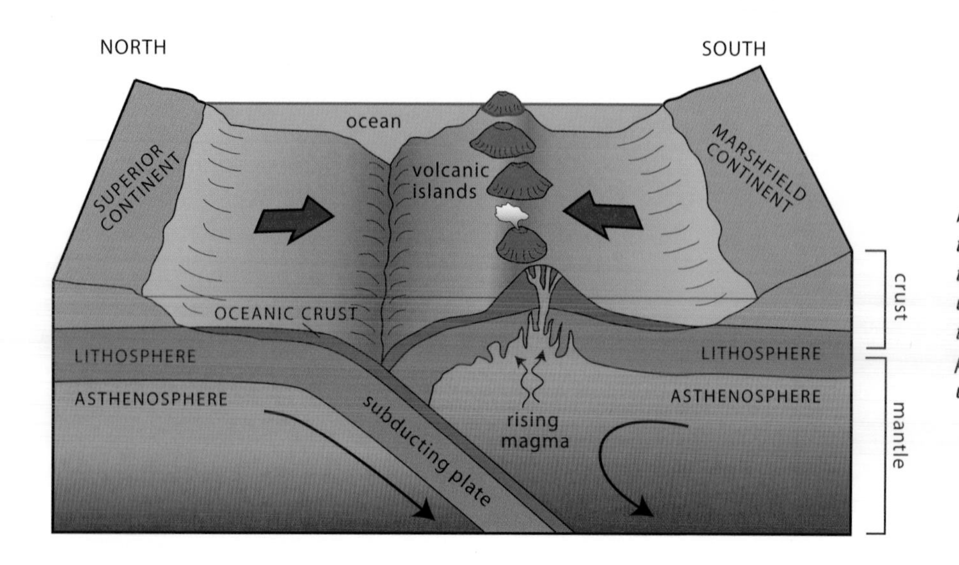

Magma erupted where the tectonic plate of the Superior continent was subducted beneath the Marshfield tectonic plate, building a chain of volcanoes in the sea.

around 1,500 million years ago when a very large body of granitic magma was intruded into the subsurface of east-central Wisconsin. It cooled to become the Wolf River Batholith.

For the next 500 million years or so following the mountain building, erosion wore down the mountains of Wisconsin. By 1,100 million years ago, most of the region was a gently rolling plain devoid of plants, so rocks and sediments were visible everywhere. At that time, the quiet period came to an end when a major plume of magma rose from the mantle and threatened to split the continent in two, in the same way the East African Rift is now pushing a piece of East Africa away from the rest of Africa. This event created the Midcontinent Rift, an arc of fractures in the crust that runs from Kansas northeast to Lake Superior, east along the length of what would later become the lake's basin, and then southeast into Michigan and possibly Ohio.

For the next 25 million years, lava flowed from the rift in spurts that created broad layers of basalt, an extrusive rock made of tiny crystals that form when lava cools quickly. Hundreds of layers of basalt, more than 25,000 feet thick in places, eventually covered what is now the bottom of the Lake Superior basin, as well as areas north and south of the lake. This period is known as Keweenawan time, named for Michigan's Keweenaw Peninsula, which extends north into Lake Superior.

While lava flowed slowly from the rift, a few volcanoes erupted more explosively in the area. The crust, stretched by the rifting process, began to subside. This sinking of the land was furthered by the weight of the growing layers of basalt,

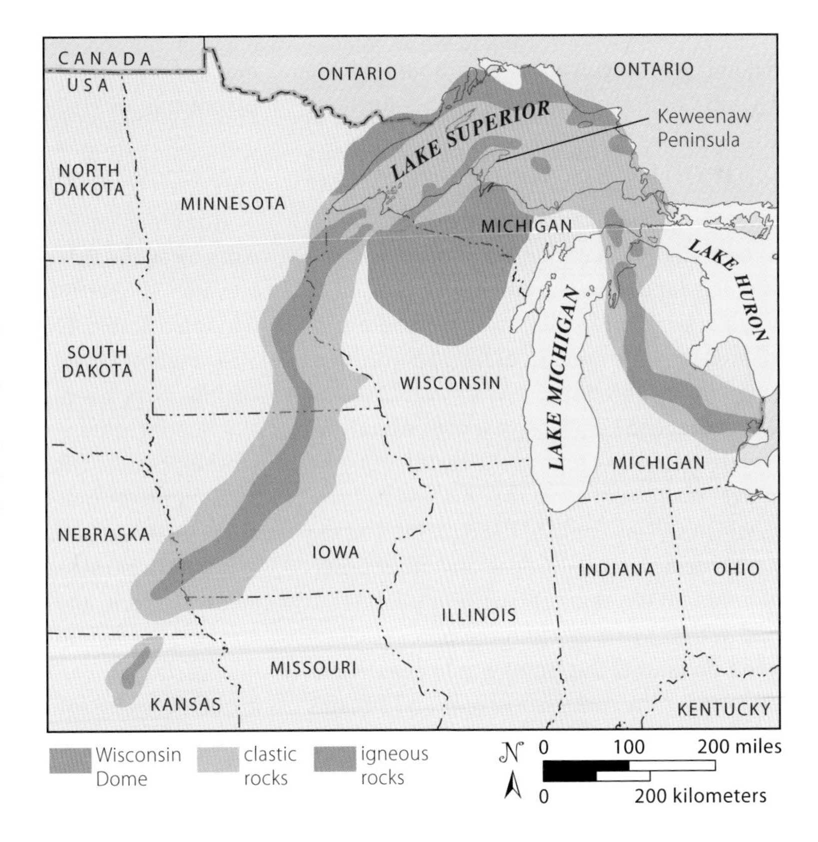

About 1,100 million years ago, the continent nearly split in two along the Midcontinent Rift, and later a region framed by the subsiding rift was uplifted, becoming the Wisconsin Dome.

which were denser than the underlying rock. The added weight of sediments brought by streams from the surrounding higher land also contributed to the subsidence, which eventually created a shallower version of the basin that now holds Lake Superior.

For some unknown reason, the rifting stopped before the continent completely split apart. It has long been thought that a continental collision to the south or southeast stopped the process, but recent evidence indicates that the rift may have simply died on its own. A study found that sandstone in the rift area was likely deformed by compression at least 100 million years after the rifting stopped, which puts the continental collision much later than geologists originally thought.

As the basin subsided, the area that is now north-central Wisconsin was gently heaved up, not dramatically but enough to create a highland called the Wisconsin Dome between the two extensions of the Midcontinent Rift. This might have been the result of the subsidence of land on either side of the dome, or it might have been part of a larger process that created a series of highlands and basins across much of the Upper Midwest. The domed area in Wisconsin is now called the Northern Highlands.

For the remainder of the Precambrian Era, erosion was the major force shaping the land. No vegetation was present to slow the erosive work of wind and water, so after hundreds of millions of years of erosion, little remains of the rock record to tell us what happened during this time.

The Cambrian Period began 541 million years ago. About that time, tropical seas were advancing toward the region from the east and west, and over millions of years they merged to cover most of Wisconsin, which still lay south of the equator. The sea was shallow, 100 to 300 feet deep, with algae and other primitive plants the predominant life-forms, along with trilobites, a variety of arthropod with a symmetrical three-part structure. Probably the only life on land at this point was lichens. Wind and rain continued to scour the rocky landscape, and streams carried sand and gravel to the seashores. The higher quartzite and rhyolite peaks stood as islands in the shallow sea.

By the end of Cambrian time, the sea had retreated, probably for the second or third time, but during the next 130 million years Paleozoic seas repeatedly invaded the region. Throughout Ordovician, Silurian, and Devonian time, each successive sea had a larger variety of life-forms whose remains collected on the seafloor. This material became limestone, as well as dolomite, a rock type that is made from limestone by the replacement of some or all of its calcium carbonate by magnesium carbonate. The technical name for this rock is dolomitic limestone, because dolomite is its principal mineral, but it is commonly referred to as dolomite. The early seas deposited thick layers of sandstone, interspersed with layers of shale and conglomerate, and later seas deposited limestone that became dolomite, again in thick layers in some places.

Geologists think that the last Paleozoic sea withdrew for good about 200 million years ago, and Wisconsin has been above sea level ever since. However, the rock record dating to about 400 million years ago has been mostly erased by erosion, with remnants of the various upper rock layers still present in only some parts of the state.

Hundreds of millions of years of uninterrupted erosion wore away the Paleozoic-age sedimentary rock on the slightly elevated Wisconsin Dome, exposing crystalline rocks of the Canadian Shield. The Paleozoic rock layers dip from the dome at a shallow angle to the west, southwest, and south and slightly more steeply to the east. The variation in rates of erosion among different rock types, a process called *differential erosion*, resulted in the edges of more resistant rock layers forming ridges that lie in roughly concentric rings around the dome on its east, south, and west sides. In many areas, they are asymmetrical ridges, called *cuestas*, with a steep side, called an *escarpment*, and a gently sloping side formed of the resistant rock layers dipping away from the dome. Lying between the cuestas, primarily on the east side of the state, are shallow lowlands where softer rock layers have been eroded away. The most prominent cuesta lies on the far east side of the state, forming the famous Niagara Escarpment, which is responsible

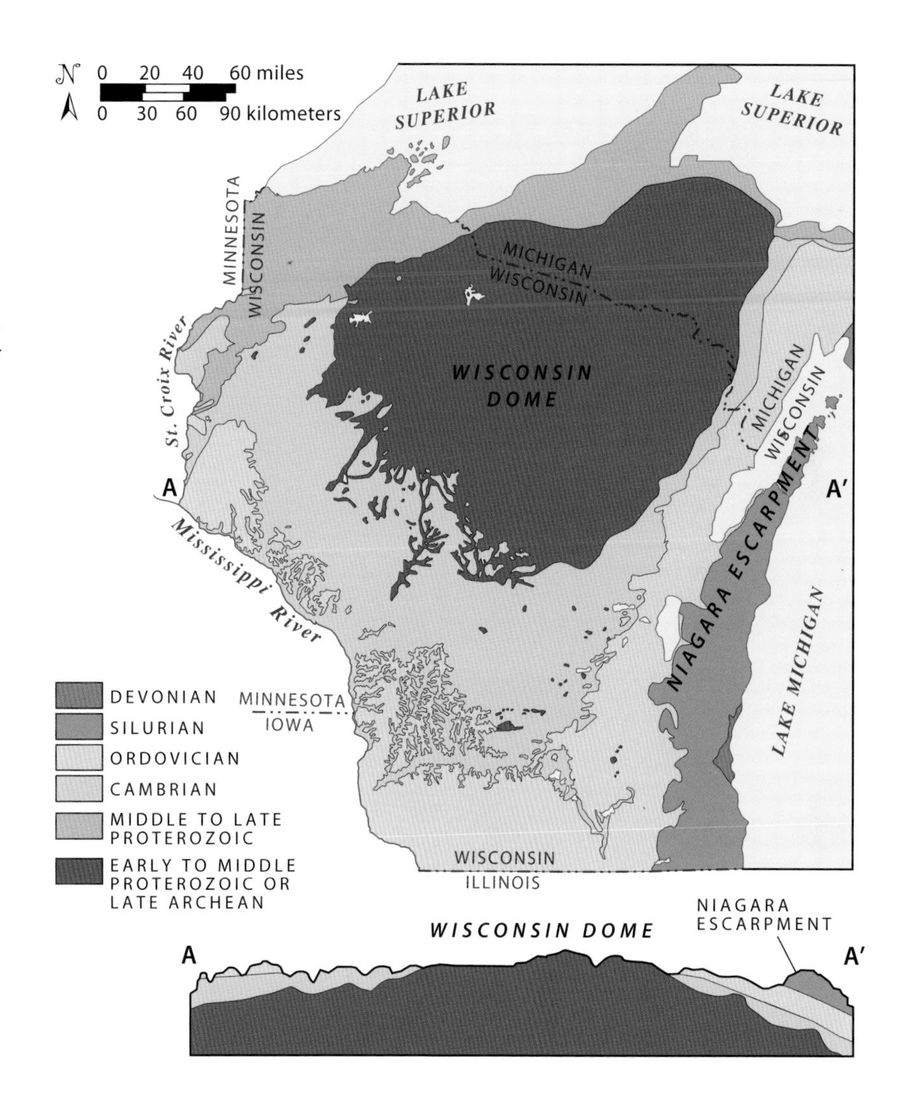

A series of cuestas have formed around the Wisconsin Dome, with rocks getting younger the farther you get from the center of the dome.—Modified from Dott and Attig, 2004

for that region's best-known land features, including the cliffs of the Door Peninsula.

At the start of the Cenozoic Era, some 65 million years ago, North America was located near its present place on the globe. It enjoyed a temperate, moist climate with well-established forests, prairies, and wetlands and a diverse array of animal life. With the coming of the Quaternary Period about 2.6 million years ago, all that changed. Due to long-term cycles having to do with Earth's tilt and orbit around the Sun, the planet cooled. In the far northern areas of the northern hemisphere, winter snow accumulation exceeded summer snowmelt. Thick layers of permanent snow turned into glaciers, or ice sheets, which are masses of ice that flow across the land, persisting over long periods of time. In the

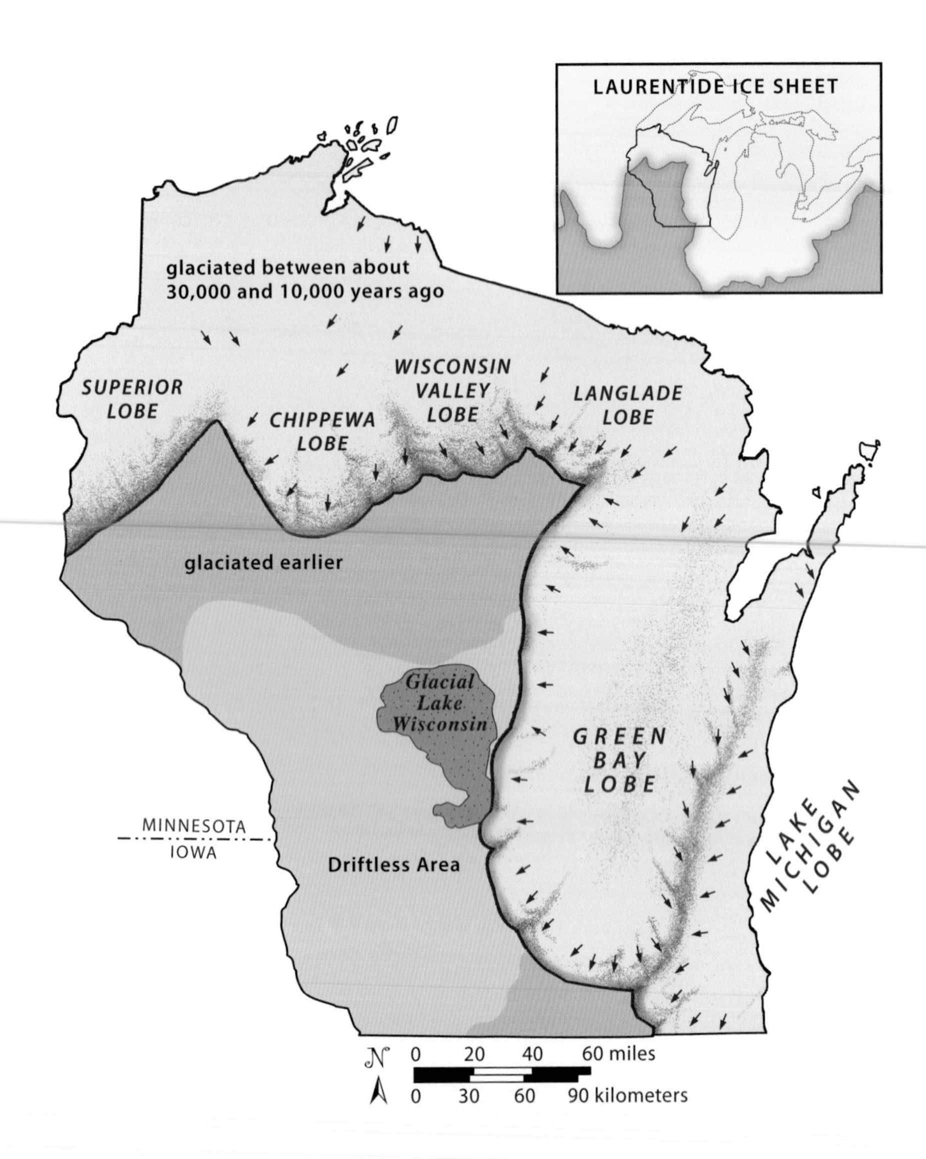

Six lobes of the ice sheet entered the state during the Wisconsin glaciation. Arrows show directions of flow of each lobe.
—Wisconsin Geological and Natural History Survey

Wisconsin region, the Laurentide ice sheet advanced and retreated an estimated ten to fifteen times.

The last advance of the ice sheet entered what is now Wisconsin about 30,000 years ago and reached its farthest southern extent by about 22,000 years ago. Because Wisconsin is a unique showcase of the effects of this glacial episode, it was named the Wisconsin glaciation. It covered the northern and eastern parts of the state with ice that was well over 1,000 feet thick at its interior, tapering to hundreds of feet thick at its margins. The glacier began retreating about 18,000 years ago and, by fits and starts, finally left the state about 10,000 years ago.

Most of the area in southwestern Wisconsin, called the Driftless Area, is thought to have been ice-free throughout the Quaternary Period. The ice extended much farther south in neighboring states, so the Driftless Area is unusual and has been studied by glaciologists from around the world.

One of the most important effects of glaciation in Wisconsin was the creation of glacial lakes—bodies of water from melting ice that were dammed on one or more sides by retreating walls of glacial ice. These lakes usually existed for many decades or centuries as the ice slowly melted. Their waves and currents eroded sand and other sediments from islands and ice-free shorelines, and the strong winds of the Quaternary Period blew dust and silt onto the lake surfaces. These sediments sank to the lake bottoms, and when the lakes drained they left behind broad plains, many of which are used today for farming.

The most recent ice sheet moved huge amounts of sand, gravel, and boulders of all sizes to create a diverse array of hills, ridges, and other landforms that are discussed in some of the stories to follow. The glacial landforms are as well preserved in Wisconsin as anywhere in the world. As the state's population and economy grew in the twentieth century, many of these land features were obliterated—plowed under for farming and urban development or mined for sand, gravel, and stone. In the 1950s, concerned scientists, educators, and citizens sought to preserve the remaining features and succeeded in passing legislation that established nine Ice Age National Scientific Reserves that are now protected from development and exploitation.

In a parallel process, the Ice Age National Scenic Trail, a proposed 1,200-mile trail along the margin of the last Pleistocene glacier, was planned and initiated in 1964. Since then, enthusiasts have worked through the Ice Age National Trail Alliance to blaze the trail on public lands and to obtain land and easements from private landowners. More than 120 segments, totaling more than 630 miles, have been constructed and maintained by volunteers, with the ultimate goal of joining them into one continuous trail.

With this very brief summary of the geologic history of Wisconsin, we can now take a tour to explore the varied landscapes and geologic features of the state. Many more details of this long and colorful history will be filled in within the stories that follow.

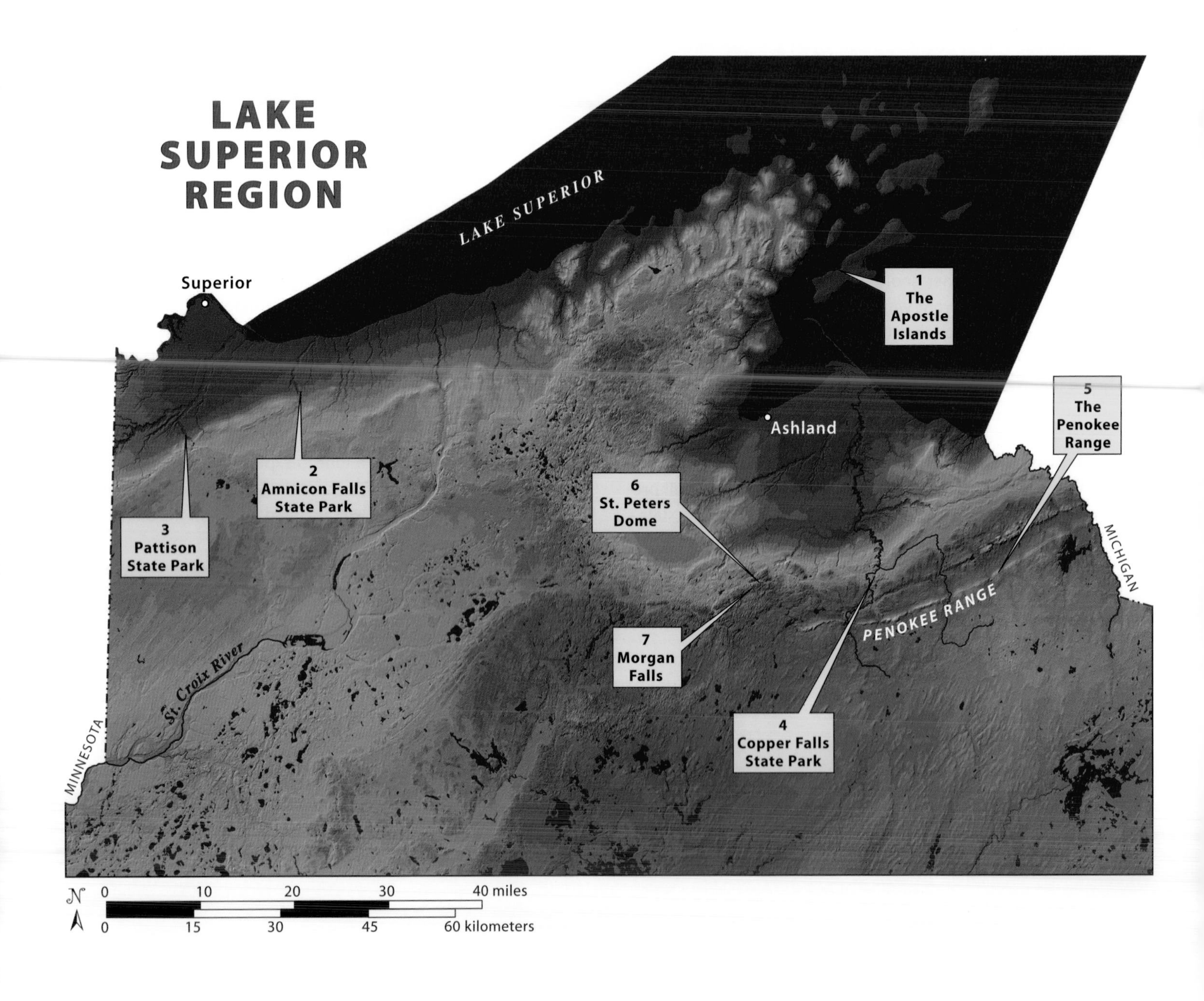
LAKE SUPERIOR REGION
LAKE SUPERIOR
Superior
Ashland
1 The Apostle Islands
2 Amnicon Falls State Park
3 Pattison State Park
4 Copper Falls State Park
5 The Penokee Range
6 St. Peters Dome
7 Morgan Falls
PENOKEE RANGE
St. Croix River
MINNESOTA
MICHIGAN
0 10 20 30 40 miles
0 15 30 45 60 kilometers
N

THE LAKE SUPERIOR REGION

Basalt, ejected as flowing lava from the Midcontinent Rift between 1,100 million and 1,060 million years ago, dominates the bedrock in the northwestern corner of Wisconsin. The presence of some rhyolite, a volcanic rock cooled from silica-rich lava, indicates that more explosive eruptions also occurred along the rift. The weight of enormous volumes of volcanic rock layers, along with the addition of sediments and the compression of the land in later Keweenawan time, led to the formation of a syncline, or downward fold resembling a trough, in which Lake Superior now resides.

Within this trough, thick deposits of sandstone interbedded with layers of basalt, conglomerate, and shale accumulated to total thicknesses of nearly 50,000 feet. The lowermost set of layers is known as the Oronto Group, composed of conglomerate, shale, siltstone, and sandstone totaling up to 17,500 feet thick. Overlying them is the Bayfield Group, composed of three formations of quartz sandstone totaling 4,300 to 7,000 feet thick. Quartz typically makes up 75 percent of the Bayfield Group. Other components, in order of importance, are orthoclase and plagioclase feldspar, mica, iron oxide (magnetite and limonite), chert, and ferromagnesian minerals. From the bottom up, the group's mostly horizontal layers include the Orienta Formation, 3,000 feet of red and white quartz sandstone containing feldspar and deposited by braided streams; the Devils Island Formation, a pink to white pure quartz sandstone, 300 feet thick, laid down under shallow ponded water, as indicated by ripple marks found in some layers; and the Chequamegon Formation, a 1,000-foot-thick red and white quartz sandstone deposited as the water receded and braided streams flowed toward the northeast. Together, the Bayfield and Oronto Groups are known locally as Lake Superior sandstones and considered to be Precambrian, although some of the uppermost layers might be as young as early Cambrian.

Compression of the land in the late Precambrian Era also caused faults—fractures in the bedrock along which adjacent blocks of land were differentially displaced. An important example that plays a prominent role in the stories to follow is the Douglas Fault, along which 1-billion-year-old basalt moved up over the much younger sandstone to the north. The fault runs from the Ashland area westward toward the Minnesota border, roughly paralleling the south shore of Lake Superior, then arcs southwest and heads toward Minneapolis. The erosion-resistant basalt forms a high escarpment today along a few sections of the fault.

The fracturing and crushing of rock along the faults created breccia, a rock made of angular shards cemented together. The faulting also exposed copper that was deposited much earlier, when hot water and gases flowing through the still-warm basaltic lava precipitated copper and other minerals in cavities within the cooling lava.

Ice age glaciers also helped forge present-day landscapes in the Lake Superior region. During the most recent glaciation, the Superior Lobe flowed southwest along the Lake Superior basin, overrunning the area and moving untold masses of rock and sand, which now mantle the bedrock. Sand and clay also settled to the bottom of meltwater lakes as the ice sheet retreated. About 10,000 years ago, meltwater ponded along the edge of the Superior Lobe as it melted back through the basin. Known as Glacial Lake Duluth, this immense body of water was up to 500 feet higher than Lake Superior is today and drained south until the ice had retreated far enough north to expose lower outlets to the east.

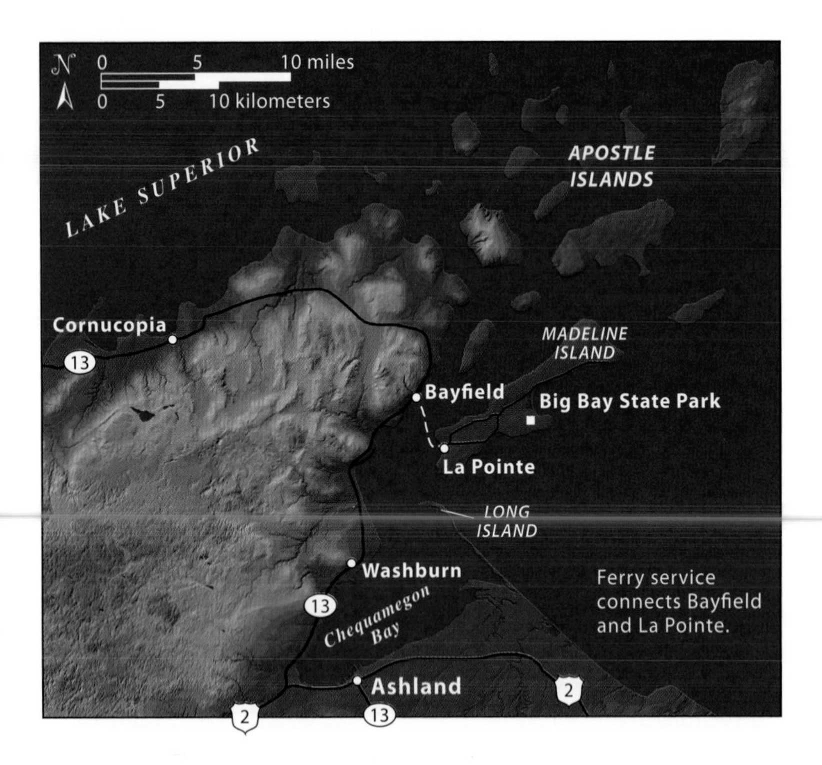

1 THE APOSTLE ISLANDS

Submerged Hills of Precambrian Sandstone

The Apostle Islands surround the northeast end of the Bayfield Peninsula, which juts from the south shore of Lake Superior. The peninsula and archipelago lie near the axis of the Midcontinent Rift basin, where the thickest layers of basalt lava and sediment accumulated after the continental rift began forming 1,100 million years ago. The uppermost and therefore youngest layers make up the Bayfield Group, mostly sandstone deposited by braided streams between 1,000 million and 600 million years ago. The braided streams flowed northeast into lakes with fluctuating water levels, but all were much smaller than today's Lake Superior.

The Bayfield sandstones, starkly visible along the shores of the Apostle Islands, are composed of grains varying in size from pebbly grits to clay. Most of the sandstone is reddish, its grains stained by iron oxide, but it also occurs in shades of pink, yellow, gray, white, and brown. A harder type, called brownstone, was quarried in the 1800s and early 1900s and valued as a building material. It forms the walls of many old buildings in area towns as well as in larger Midwestern cities.

During the ice age, repeated incursions of an ice sheet from the northeast, starting around 2 million years ago, gouged the lake basin deeper and chipped away at a peninsula's mass of sandstone. During the most recent ice advance between 30,000 and 10,000 years ago, this sandstone mass split one part of the ice sheet into two lobes—the Superior Lobe to the northwest and the Chippewa Lobe to the southeast. Subglacial streams contributed to the glacial erosion, deepening the valleys between the high hills of the peninsula. The archipelago of twenty-two islands is a continuation of the peninsula's hills, but here they are largely submerged, with high points ranging from 20 to 500 feet above the lake surface.

Since the glacial retreat, the waves and currents of Lake Superior and its predecessors, starting with Glacial Lake Duluth, have continued sculpting the islands. A spectacular array of sandstone cliffs, arches, pillars, caves, and gleaming sand beaches dress the perimeters of the islands, drawing thousands of summer visitors in kayaks, sailboats, and cruisers. The largest, Madeline Island, is developed and inhabited year-round, with ferry service between the little town of La Pointe and the Bayfield Peninsula during warm months and a road across the ice during winter. La Pointe has a long history of settlement dating back to when it was the site of a Native American village in the 1600s.

Long Island, the one island that is not made of sandstone, is part of a sand spit that developed after the glacier retreated. Waves and currents built the spit, which originally stretched northwest from the eastern headland of Chequamegon Bay, forming the harbor for Ashland. A few of Lake Superior's ferocious storms washed away part of the spit, creating the gap that separates Long Island from the mainland spit.

This reddish sandstone of the Bayfield Group is common in the shoreline cliffs of several of the islands.

The beach at Big Bay State Park on Madeline Island.

2 AMNICON FALLS STATE PARK

The Douglas Fault Escarpment

The 30-mile-long Amnicon River gets its name from an Ojibwe word meaning "where fish spawn," and the mouth of the river on Lake Superior's south shore is indeed an important spawning site. In the 2-mile stretch across Amnicon Falls State Park, the river drops 180 feet in a series of beautiful and geologically interesting waterfalls.

Upper Falls cascades 30 feet over the Douglas Fault escarpment, where hard, erosion-resistant igneous rock is juxtaposed against softer, more easily eroded sedimentary rock. The rock ledge under the falls is 1.1-billion-year-old, dark-colored basalt, cooled from lava that erupted from the Midcontinent Rift a few dozen miles to the north. The basalt under the falls is brown because weathering has oxidized the surface to limonite, a commonly occurring iron oxide. Close examination of the very subtle differences in coloration reveals layers in the basalt, which represent separate flows of lava. Downstream from the falls, the riverbanks are lighter-colored, clearly layered sandstone, much younger than the basalt that heaved up at the fault. Between the sandstone and basalt is a 12-foot breccia zone, made of shards of basalt pulverized by the faulting action and cemented together over time. Next to this zone, a section of sandstone was tipped up to a nearly vertical position, also by the faulting.

Two other falls flow over the Douglas Fault escarpment, which runs east to west across the park. On the south branch of the Amnicon River, Snake Pit Falls is a ferocious cataract in spring, when the water is high, but usually slows to a trickle in later summer. In contrast, Now-and-Then Falls displays a different sort of beauty as a gentle, braided flow—a trickling descent of a smaller third branch of the river that runs only during the high-water season.

The main, central branch of the river downstream from Upper Falls flows within a canyon of Lake Superior sandstone. Joints, or vertical cracks, in the sandstone have played a major role in the canyon formation. As the river erodes the sandstone layers at water level, the overlying layers separate from the larger mass at one of these joints and fall into the river.

The river removed much of the glacial till from the park area, but large boulders, called glacial erratics, remain, carried here by the glacier from as far north as Canada. Look for boulders of metamorphic granite gneiss and reddish volcanic rhyolite. On some horizontal basalt outcroppings near the river, you can also find glaciation striations, or scratches, made by hard stones trapped in the bottom of the glacier.

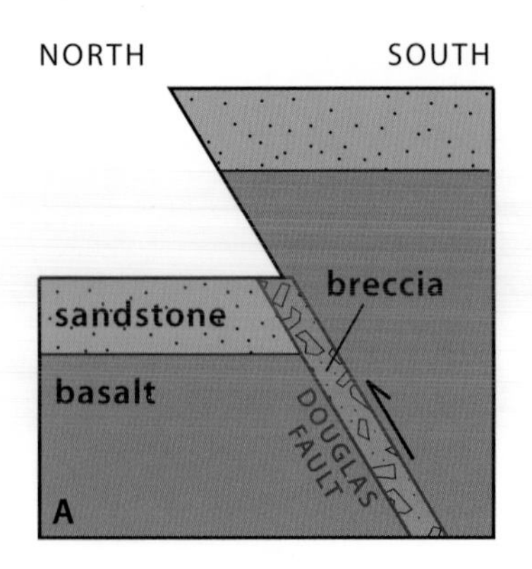

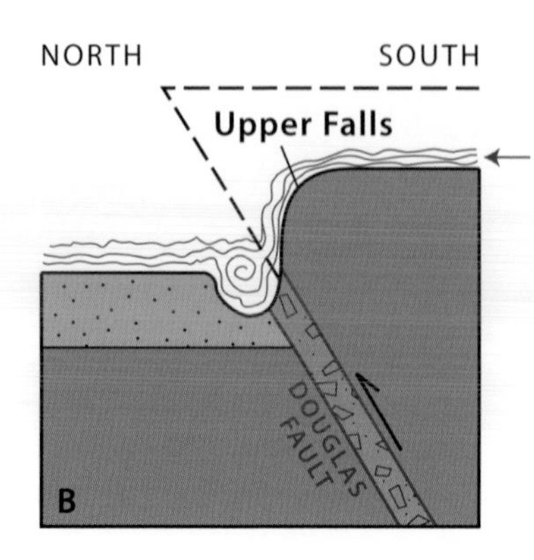

The Douglas Fault juxtaposes the basalt against the sandstone at Upper Falls. Dashed line in B represents eroded rock.

Upper Falls cascades over basalt on its way to a pool lined with sandstone.

Brecciated basalt in the fault zone just downstream of Upper Falls.

At Lower Falls, the Amnicon River flows over a ledge of well-bedded Lake Superior sandstone, undermining it.

Upstream from the big falls, Little Manitou Falls flows over dark basalt. The Black River's root beer color is due to tannins and other organic acids in the river, picked up in vast wetlands in its headwaters.

3 PATTISON STATE PARK

Wisconsin's Highest Waterfall Plunges over Keweenawan Basalt

The chief attraction at Pattison State Park is Big Manitou Falls, Wisconsin's highest waterfall and the fourth highest east of the Rocky Mountains. The Black River, one of several relatively short rivers that drain the Northern Highlands and flow into Lake Superior, plummets 165 feet where it crosses the Douglas Fault. The escarpment along the fault is made of basalt more than 1 billion years old that was heaved up above the much younger sandstone to the north. The basalt walls near the waterfall have a noticeably brownish color—the stain of oxidation caused largely by limonite, a commonly occurring iron oxide.

As the Wisconsin ice sheet retreated north more than 10,000 years ago, it left behind a moraine—a pile of glacial debris that accumulated at the margin of the glacier. The moraine lay parallel to the south shore of Lake Superior and covered the Douglas Fault escarpment. Glacial Lake Duluth also covered the escarpment, leaving behind a thick layer of lake bed clay. The Black River, flush with glacial meltwater, rapidly cut through the clay and moraine and then went to work eroding the bedrock. The river found a route along a cross fault, a short fault lying at an angle to the main Douglas Fault. The zone of breccia along the cross fault, shards of basalt shattered by the faulting action and cemented together over time, is less resistant than the surrounding mass of basalt, so the falls has migrated upstream along it to the main fault. About 1.5 miles upstream of Big Manitou Falls is Little Manitou Falls, which plunges over a 31-foot-tall ledge of basalt into another breccia zone along another small fault associated with the Douglas Fault system.

Downstream of the fault and Big Manitou Falls, the river created a 100-to-170-foot gorge in the bedded sandstone of the Bayfield Group, which is much younger than the basalt ledge at the Douglas Fault. At one of the vantage points on the park's geology walk (for which a guidebook is available in the park office), visitors can see where the fault is located—downstream from the big falls, which has since migrated upstream.

Before European immigration, the Native Americans in the area were the Ojibwe, who called the falls Gitchi Monido, for the Great Spirit whose voice they heard in the roar of the falls. Manitou is a variation of that name, probably invented by an early French explorer. Native American groups collected copper from the park area between 6,000 and 500 years ago, using it for decorative items, tools, and weapons. Later, European immigrants attempted to mine copper commercially without much success.

A wall of Bayfield Group sandstone downstream from Big Manitou Falls in the gorge at Pattison State Park.

Big Manitou Falls cascades down the basalt escarpment upstream from the Douglas Fault.

COPPER FALLS STATE PARK

A Meeting of Rivers in the Breccia of Fault Zones

At Copper Falls State Park a complex set of ridges surrounds a deep gorge where the Tyler Forks and Bad Rivers meet, a confluence of spectacular waterfalls, whirlpools, and rock formations. Over the past 2 million years, multiple ice sheets covered the park area. The most recent, the Chippewa Lobe, left a deep layer of sandy till called the Copper Falls Formation. As the glacier withered away around 11,500 years ago, Glacial Lake Duluth inundated most of this area for more than 200 years. Evidence of ancient beaches in the park indicates the highest ridges might have been islands in the lake. When the glacial lake drained, it left behind a deep layer of red clay, known as the Miller Creek Formation, which is evident in the northern part of the park.

Hidden beneath the glacial sediments are ancient rocks of the Midcontinent Rift. The volcanic bedrock in the park includes mostly basalt from the rift, along with some andesite and rhyolite—the extrusive equivalents of diorite and granite—that erupted from a large volcano around 1,100 million years ago. During many millions of years following this volcanic activity, streams flowing primarily northeast toward the rift basin deposited sediments that became layers of red and brown conglomerate, sandstone, and siltstone (the Copper Harbor Conglomerate); gray and black shale, siltstone, and mudstone (the Nonesuch Formation, deposited in a shallow body of water); and red and brown interbedded sandstone and conglomerate (the Freda Sandstone, deposited by rivers). These formations are part of the Oronto Group that filled the rift basin.

These sedimentary layers dipped gently northwest into the Lake Superior rift basin until 1,060 million years ago, when they

The Copper Falls Formation includes reddish-brown sand and gravel till deposited by the Wisconsin glaciation. It is up to 148 feet thick.

The Bad River enters the photo at bottom left. The Tyler Forks River enters at right, cascading over Brownstone Falls (partially hidden by trees). The combined rivers flow through the notch in the volcanic rock toward the upper left.

The right side of Copper Falls on the Bad River is 29 feet high. On its east side (left), the river has eroded the bank enough to cause large slabs of basalt to drop onto the ledge, collapsing the bank to less than half the height it was when the park was established.

were tilted dramatically more to the north and northwest by a distant continental collision to the east, the Grenville Orogeny. The compression caused the layers to shift and slide over one another along faults, pulverizing rock at the contacts between the layers. Over time, resistant layers became ridges and less-resistant layers eroded, creating the crazy quilt topography of the park. The valleys often lie in zones of fault breccia.

Geologists estimate that early versions of the rivers that now meet in the park were flowing as far back as 200 million years ago. The flowing water wore away at the breccia zones, carving a gorge that ranges from 65 to 120 feet deep. You can hike along the rim of the gorge to see Copper Falls, where the Bad River plunges 29 feet over a basalt ledge into a breccia zone. Farther downstream in the gorge is Brownstone Falls, where the Tyler Forks River cascades across basalt ridges and then drops 30 feet to the confluence with the Bad River, where the waters meet in a huge whirlpool. On the north side of this confluence is a high wall of red lava rock—a rhyolite mass over 900 feet thick. This resistant rock has caused the Bad River to veer 90 degrees to the northwest, where the combined waters carved a notch in the volcanic rock. Beyond the notch the river flattens out to a much more docile flow, meandering toward Lake Superior.

Downstream from the confluence, a trail takes hikers to the Devil's Gate, an upended wall of sedimentary rock of the Oronto Group that shows vividly how the rock layers were tilted 86 degrees to the northwest. The vertical layers of conglomerate, shale, and sandstone were forged from ancient deposits of gravel, mud, and sand, respectively. The Bad River continues eroding this wall every spring when it flows high and fast.

The park's volcanic rocks contain small deposits of copper, but this is not the reason for the name of Copper Falls. It refers to the copper-colored water in the river, which is due to the presence of tannins leached into the water from large peaty bogs at the river's source. Native Americans of the Old Copper Culture mined the shallow copper deposits for hundreds of years, using the copper to make decorative items, tools, and hunting weapons. European immigrant miners tried unsuccessfully to mine copper on a larger scale in the 1860s, and the effects of their digging and blasting can be found in the park.

The main loop trail to the falls and Devil's Gate is called the Doughboys' Trail, named for World War I veterans who were enlisted to build it in 1920 and 1921. They and the Civilian Conservation Corps workers of the 1930s built some of the finest trails, bridges, and stone staircases in Wisconsin's parks.

Upended layers of sedimentary rock of the Oronto Group at Devil's Gate.

5 THE PENOKEE RANGE

Iron Mines in Upended Precambrian Rock Layers

Stretching 80 miles west to east across a part of far northern Wisconsin and the Upper Peninsula of Michigan is a range of prominent hills called the Gogebic Range, named for the lake on its eastern end. The range is up to 3 miles wide, although the Wisconsin portion, commonly called the Penokees, is generally less than 1 mile wide. These hills stand 100 to 600 feet above the lowlands to the north and south. The range's highest point, with an elevation of 1,872 feet, is Mt. Whittlesey, located a few miles southeast of Mellen, Wisconsin, at the western end of the range.

Mt. Whittlesey is named for Charles Whittlesey, a geologist and retired army officer who studied the Penokees in the mid-1800s. Apparently, he intended to call these hills the Pewabic Range, using the Ojibwe word for "iron," but errors in the translation of his notes at the government printing office led to the name Penokee. Whittlesey's intended name was appropriate because the range contains an extensive deposit of iron, the most valuable of which has been mined. Because of the cost of removing the remaining deposits and the potential environmental damage that would likely result, there has been no mining in this range since the 1960s.

A parallel but lower range of hills lies just to the northwest of the Penokees. Sometimes mistaken for being part of the Gogebic Range, or Penokee Range, these hills are the Trap Range, or Gabbro Range. They are composed of a different set of rock than the Penokees, primarily Keweenawan basalt and intrusive gabbro, locally called "black granite." The Trap Range contains no iron formations.

You can view the Penokee Range from several places, some of which require a little hiking. On County Highway GG a few

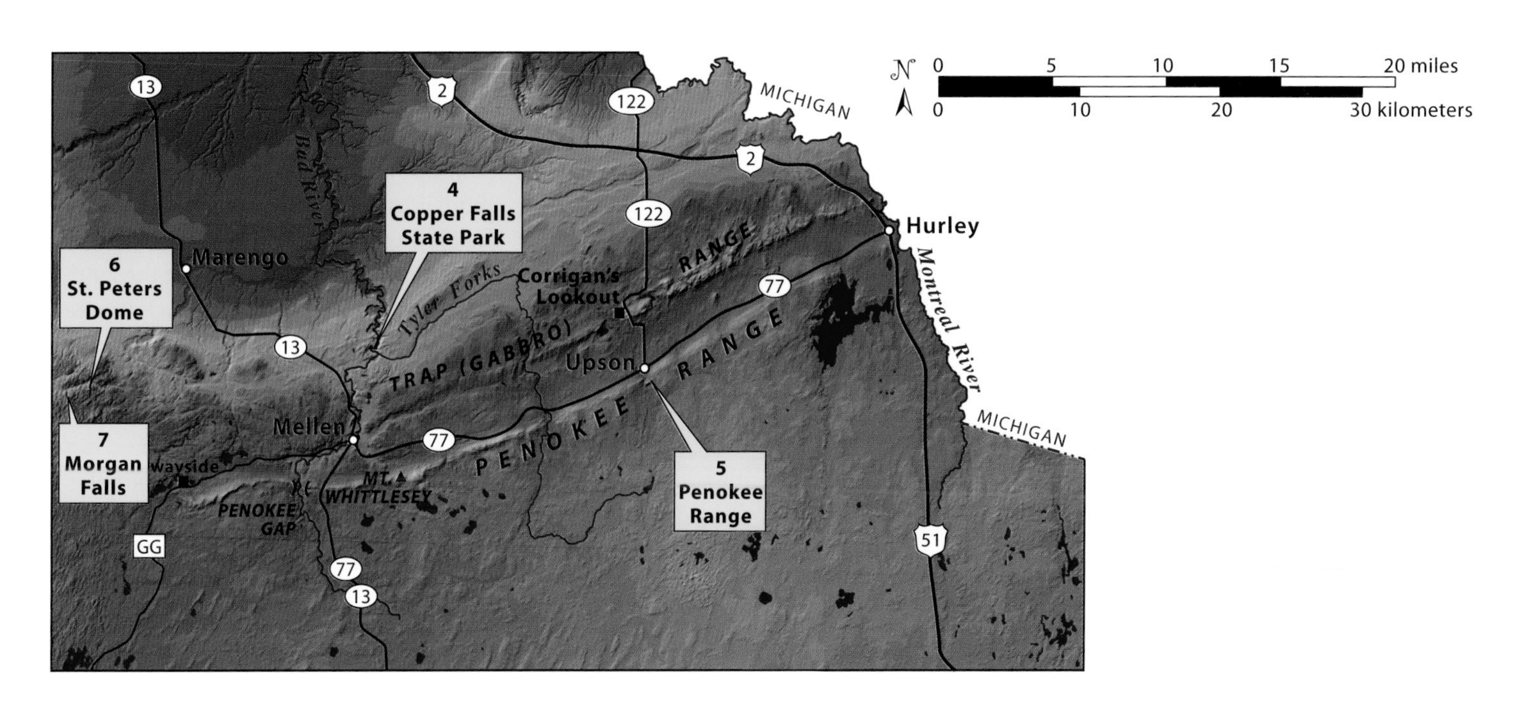

miles west of Mellen, a wayside has a boardwalk and staircases leading to a viewing platform built on a rocky overlook with a view from north of the range. Another viewpoint is Corrigan's Lookout, located in the Gabbro Range. The lookout is just east of WI 122, about 2 miles north of Upson, and involves a fairly steep 0.3-mile hike.

The Penokees (in distance) viewed from Corrigan's Lookout to the north of the range. The hills in the foreground are the Trap Range.

Tailings pile from iron mining near Montreal, Wisconsin.

The Penokee Range is made of upended layers of sedimentary rock deposited between 2,300 and 1,850 million years ago. Streams flowing into shallow Precambrian seas deposited sand, gravel, and mud over the top of Archean greenstones and granites and Bad River Dolomite. The sediments became sandstone, conglomerate, and shale, respectively.

Sediments rich in iron were also deposited in shallow seas around 1,890 to 1,850 million years ago. At this time, the planet's atmosphere lacked today's oxygen levels because plants, with their oxygen-producing process, did not yet exist on land. In such oxygen-deficient conditions, iron was soluble and present in large amounts in the ocean waters, so it became incorporated in the sedimentary rock.

During the Penokean mountain building episode, between 1,890 and 1,830 million years ago, the layers that make up the Penokees were metamorphosed and tilted to the northwest. (The Penokean episode was named for the Penokee Range.) When the Lake Superior rift basin formed and deepened, beginning about 1,100 million years ago, the tilted rock layers pitched further to the northwest. During the compression of the land that followed the rifting, the rock layers were heaved up further still to nearly 90 degrees to the north-northwest.

The southeast side of the Penokee Range is tilted rock of the Palms Formation, 450 to 550 feet of quartzite, conglomerate, and slate. The next layer to the northwest, formerly on top of the now upended Palms Formation, is the Ironwood Formation, a 650-foot-thick set of interbedded iron-rich and silica-rich layers lying on the northwest side of the range. The Palms and Ironwood Formations are extremely hard, resistant rocks, so they make up the high ridge. Since early Paleozoic time, streams have worked their way along faults, eroding several gaps in the ridge, making it more of a range of elongated hills. The Penokee Gap is southwest of Mellen, where the Bad River cuts through the Penokees on its northerly course toward Lake Superior.

The iron mining industry thrived in the Penokees between 1884 and 1965. Unlike the horizontal deposits of Minnesota's famous Mesabi Range, the Penokee deposits were vertical, so miners had to use shafts and tunnels, while piling waste rock on the surface. The deepest of these subsurface mines was 4,335 feet deep. Several mining towns sprang up in the lowland on the north side of the Penokees. The lowland is eroded in the Tyler Slate, a less-resistant formation in the upended Precambrian sedimentary rock. The Iron County Historical Museum in Hurley has a display on the history of iron mining in the Penokees. *Discovering the Penokees*, a book of photos by Joel Austin, with essays by various writers, captures the rugged beauty of the range, with its pristine forests laced with thousands of spring-fed streams.

Iron-bearing rock from the Penokee Range. —Specimen on display at the University of Wisconsin Geology Museum

Close-up of gabbro, also known as "black granite."

An outcrop of gabbro just north of Mellen on the east side of WI 13.

6 ST. PETERS DOME

Pink Granite of the Mellen Complex

St. Peters Dome, a high rock outcropping in the middle of a dense, older forest, is popular among hikers for its remote, pristine nature and spectacular views of the region. Located about 15 miles south of Ashland, the dome sits at 1,560 feet above sea level, 400 feet above the floor of the Morgan Creek gorge, in which the trail to the outcropping lies. On a clear day, hikers can see Ashland, Chequamegon Bay, the Bayfield Peninsula, and sometimes even the Apostle Islands to the north, as well as the Penokees to the south. All around the dome is a vast expanse of mostly unbroken forest cover, part of the Chequamegon-Nicolet National Forest. This rare old-growth and second-growth northern hardwood forest, one of the best-preserved tracts of Wisconsin's Northwoods, includes primarily maple, basswood, ash, aspen, and birch.

St. Peters Dome, locally known as Old Baldy, is northwest of the line of hills known as the Penokees but is on similar terrain. The ancient bedrock is a mix of igneous, metamorphic, and volcanic rock. Overlying the bedrock is 40 inches or more of glacial till, mostly sandy to loamy soil. The 1.8-mile trail to the dome runs through the moist, rocky gorge of Morgan Creek before rising to higher, drier land south of the gorge and then ascending the precipice. This trail is fairly rugged and requires sturdy footwear. Most of the prominent outcroppings in the gorge are composed of pink granite, as is St. Peters Dome. This fine-grained granite, called granophyre, was intruded as large sills, or horizontal layers, into volcanic flows of the Mellen Complex about 1.1 billion years ago. Named for the nearby city of Mellen, the complex is composed largely of basalts of the Midcontinent Rift, along with granite and gabbro intrusions.

The view to the west-northwest from St. Peters Dome.

The pink granite of St. Peters Dome.

7 MORGAN FALLS

A Billion-Year-Old Granite Ledge

Morgan Falls, the state's third-highest waterfall, is located northwest of the Penokee Range and about 1 mile west of St. Peters Dome. This secluded waterfall drops 70 feet from the top of its upper cascade to the floor of the Morgan Creek gorge. While some sources say Morgan Creek flows over the falls, it is actually an unnamed tributary that drops into the canyon on a short course to Morgan Creek. It flows along a diagonally oriented ledge across a 1.1-billion-year-old granite escarpment.

The rock faces in this canyon appear to be jumbled because the falls is located at the juncture of three faults—the Keweenaw thrust fault to the east and the Crystal Lake–Atkins Lake and Owen thrust faults to the west. The ledge over which the water cascades is near a contact between a fine-grained quartz granite and a body of gabbro, a dark intrusive igneous rock. The gorge around the falls is protected in order to preserve an unusual microclimate that supports a variety of ferns, mosses, and lichens, some of them rare. In order to preserve the pristine beauty here, visitors are urged to stay on the trail and to not climb on or around the falls.

Morgan Falls drops diagonally along a ledge of 1.1-billion-year-old granite.

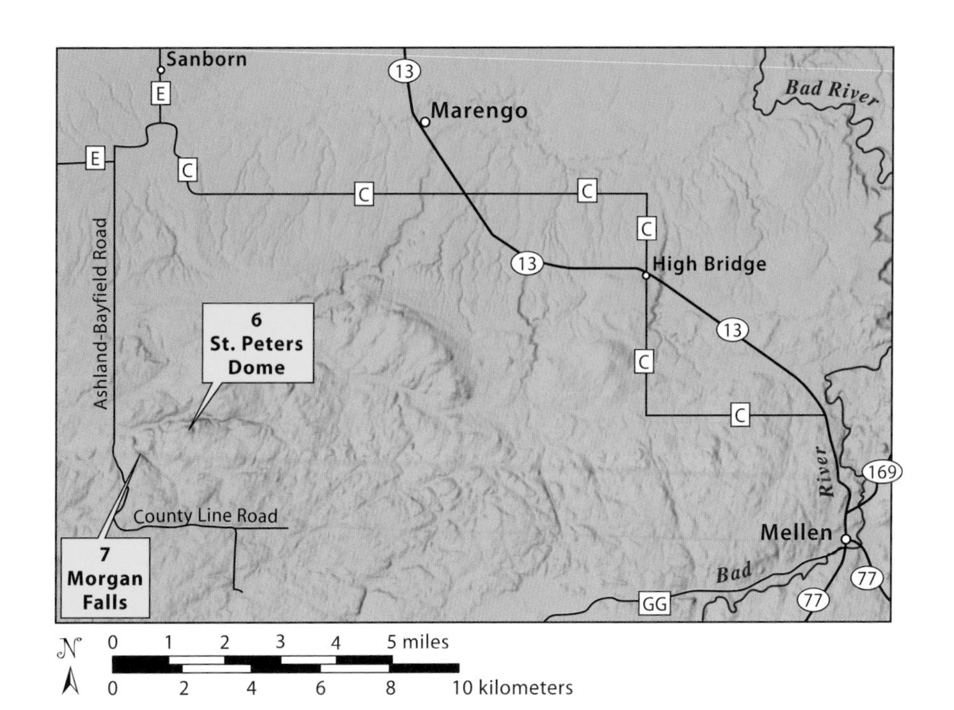

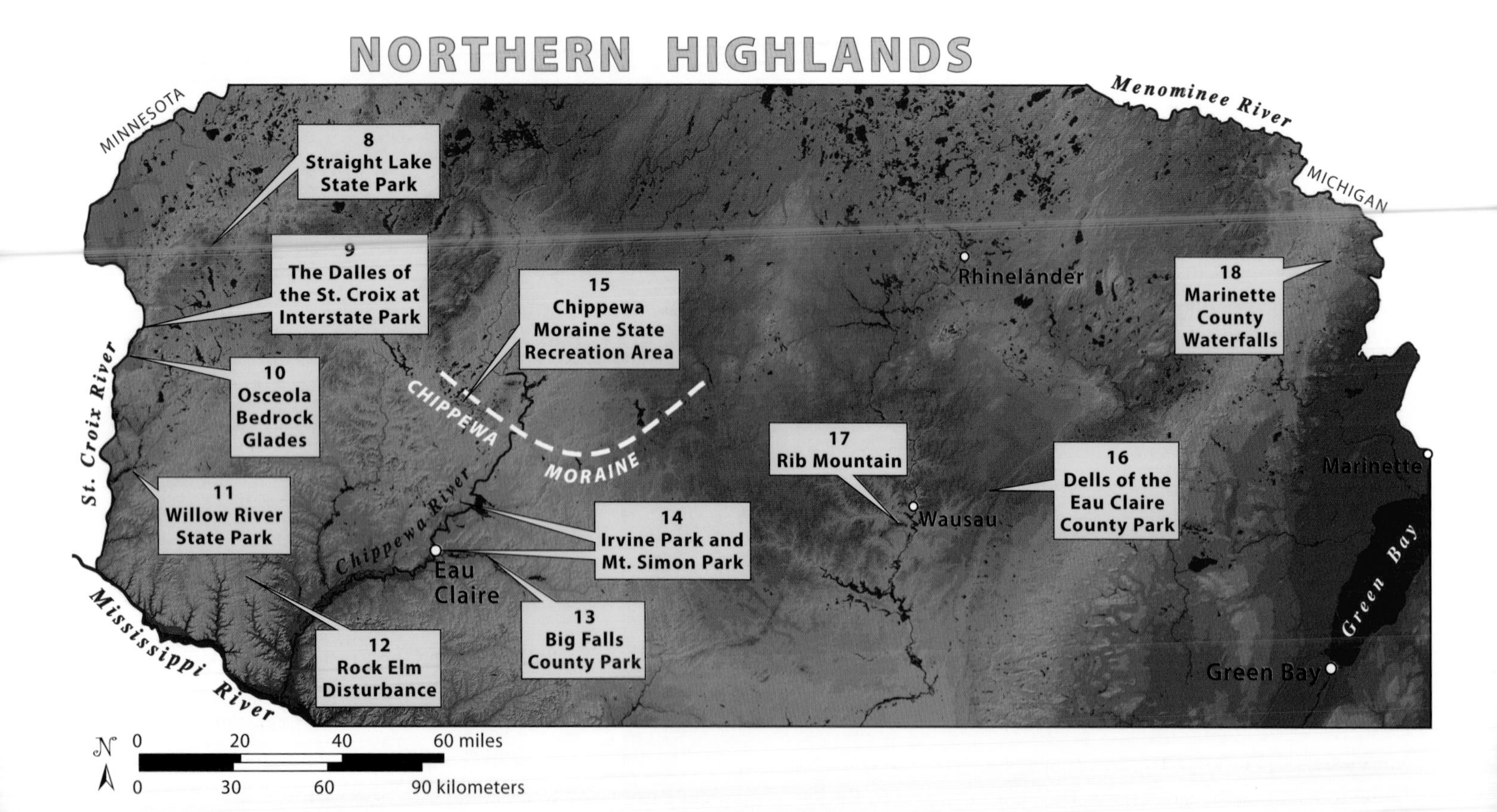
NORTHERN HIGHLANDS
MINNESOTA
Menominee River
MICHIGAN
8
Straight Lake
State Park
9
The Dalles of
the St. Croix at
Interstate Park
15
Chippewa
Moraine State
Recreation Area
Rhinelander
18
Marinette
County
Waterfalls
St. Croix River
10
Osceola
Bedrock
Glades
CHIPPEWA
MORAINE
17
Rib Mountain
16
Dells of the
Eau Claire
County Park
Marinette
11
Willow River
State Park
Chippewa River
14
Irvine Park and
Mt. Simon Park
Wausau
Eau
Claire
Green Bay
Mississippi River
12
Rock Elm
Disturbance
13
Big Falls
County Park
Green Bay
N
0
20
40
60 miles
0
30
60
90 kilometers

THE NORTHERN HIGHLANDS

Northern Wisconsin lies on the southern edge of the Canadian Shield—the core of the ancient continent of North America. Sometime during or after the development of the Midcontinent Rift, north-central Wisconsin was warped up slightly into the Wisconsin Dome. When the last of the Paleozoic seas had departed, Wisconsin was completely covered with interbedded layers of sandstone, shale, and dolomite. Within 200 million years, the uppermost layers had been eroded from the slightly higher dome, creating a roughly circular region of exposed Precambrian rock.

The glaciers of the Quaternary Period furthered this erosion, breaking up and abrading softer rock as they moved south. Much of the debris, including silt, sand, gravel, and boulders, was incorporated into the moving ice, and dust and sand blown by wind collected on top of the glaciers. Inching across the land for thousands of years, these dynamic ice sheets collected huge volumes of such sediments. During warming trends and seasonal thawing, rivers and lakes formed atop these ice masses, covering the ice with sediment. Ice mantled by thicker layers of debris tended to melt more slowly than ice exposed to sunlight. Thus a landscape of sorts, including peaks, ridges, and valleys, developed on top of each ice mass, with the valleys collecting more debris over time.

At the end of the glacial period, as the climate warmed, the ice slowly melted. The debris on top of and within the ice was dropped upon the newly ice-free land, forming a blanket of loose sediment called *glacial till*. The resulting landscape was generally a reversal of the icescape that had existed atop the glaciers. That is, a peak or ridge made mostly of ice melted away completely and left little or no till on the land. A valley in the ice full of sand, gravel, and boulders dropped its load on the land, creating an uneven ridge of sediment that stood above the surrounding area. This glacial process is known as *topographic reversal*.

Prominent glacial landforms, including moraines, moulin kames, eskers, tunnel channels, kettles, and hummocky terrain, resulted from the slow process of melting. These and other glacial landforms, on display at several sites in the Northern Highlands, are explained in the stories to follow.

8 STRAIGHT LAKE STATE PARK

Tunnel Channel beneath the Ice

Northeast of the town of Luck is a long, straight, mostly undeveloped valley that represents one of the world's finest examples of a tunnel channel. A meltwater stream flowing beneath a glacier formed the channel. Up to half-a-mile wide, the 7.5-mile-long forested valley is as deep as 90 feet below the average level of the land on either side of it. Segments of the Ice Age National Scenic Trail lie within the tunnel channel and along its rims.

About 15,000 years ago, the Superior Lobe of the continental ice sheet occupied this part of the state but was disintegrating as the climate warmed. Hundreds of subglacial streams of meltwater carved tunnels through the base of the melting ice mass before emerging from beneath the margin of the glacier. The southeast side of the Superior Lobe curved across the Northern Highlands, and the streams flowed generally southeast. Most of these stream valleys were buried in glacial debris as the melting ice dropped its load of sand and gravel. Others were obliterated by human development of the land. Only a few are clearly visible today.

Because of the sheer mass of the glacier and the growing volume of water within the melting ice mass, the water in subglacial tunnels was under great pressure. These streams at times gushed through the tunnels with enough force to move large boulders and scour any sediment from the bedrock surface. A typical stream carried a large volume of sand and gravel, and as its flow eventually slowed it deposited this glacial debris along the length of its bedrock tunnel floor. When the ice finally shrank away, it left long ridges of sediment, called *eskers*, where the streams had flowed.

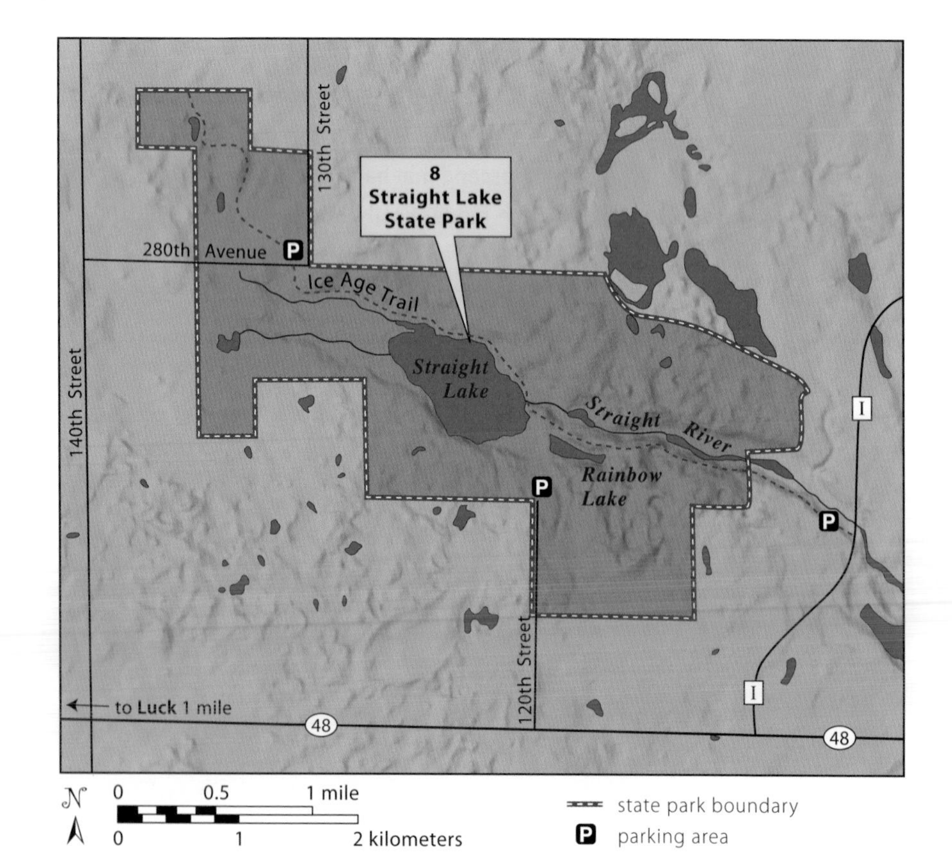

The best way to see the Straight Lake tunnel channel and its remarkable features is to access the Ice Age Trail at a trailhead on 280th Avenue, 2.5 miles east of WI 35 and north of Luck. (There are two other trail access points within the undeveloped Straight Lake State Park.) About 1 mile north of this trailhead, the Ice Age Trail crosses a valley of moss-covered boulders (mostly basalt) up to 5 feet in diameter. The train of fractured bedrock boulders—about 30 feet wide and 50 yards long—was brought there by the gushing subglacial stream that carved the Straight Lake tunnel channel to the southeast. Also

A subglacial stream, flowing toward this vantage point from the west, created this tunnel channel.

along the trail at this point are dramatic outcroppings of bedrock basalt exposed by postglacial erosion.

Throughout the area are glacial erratics —boulders of red granite, rhyolite, and diorite—some of which are thought to have come from north of Lake Superior. South of the Ice Age Trail trailhead, the trail drops into the tunnel channel, which contains Straight Lake and Rainbow Lake, both kettle lakes; the Straight River, which flows the length of the tunnel channel; and several small kettle lakes and wetlands. Sections of an esker lie within much of the channel, and the trail winds up, along, and over the esker for good views of the tunnel channel and its features. On either side of the valley is hummocky terrain, all well preserved within the boundaries of the state park.

Outcrops of 1-billion-year-old basalt at Straight Lake.

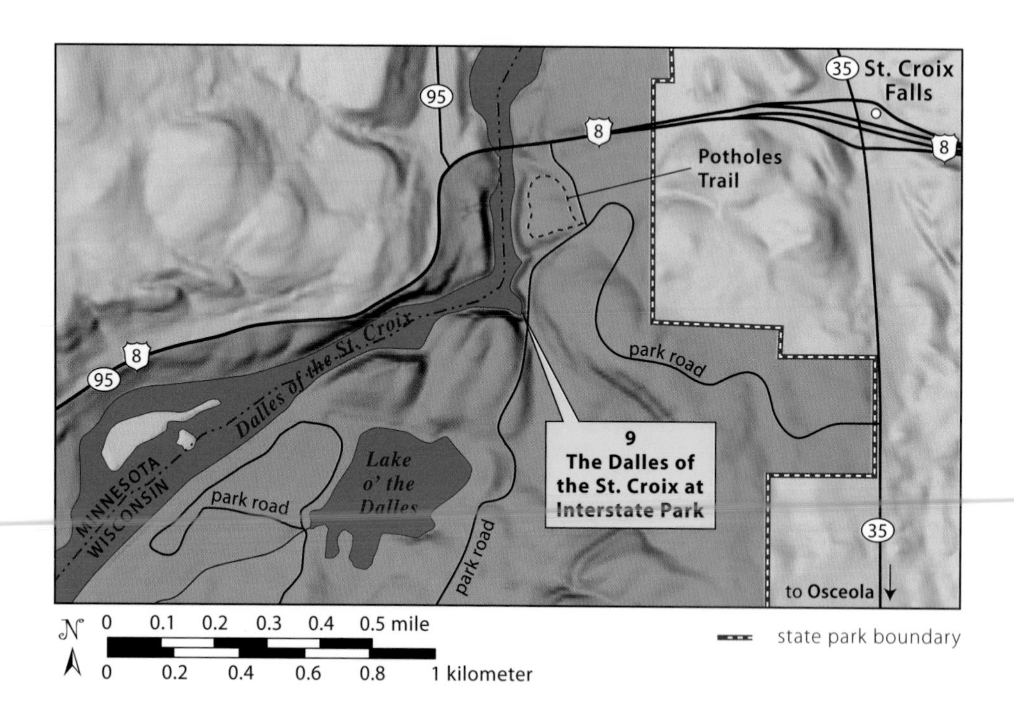

9 THE DALLES OF THE ST. CROIX AT INTERSTATE PARK

Potholes Carved by Glacial Flood

Interstate Park, straddling the St. Croix River on the Wisconsin-Minnesota border, is famous for its potholes—vertical holes carved into the bedrock of the ancient riverbed. The bedrock here is multiple layers of basalt, each a lava flow erupted from the Midcontinent Rift, which ran through the park area. These eruptions began 1.1 billion years ago and continued for 25 million years or more, piling up a layered mass of basalt as much as 4 miles thick. Near the north end of the park, where the river flows south and veers west at a nearly 90-degree bend, is a deep, narrow canyon, called the Dalles of the St. Croix, carved through this basalt mass. *Dalles*, a French word that means "slabs," has come to mean a steep-sided, narrow canyon containing a stream.

During the Wisconsin glaciation, a 1,000-foot-thick lobe of ice covered the park. As the glacier retreated from the area between 16,000 and 10,000 years ago, meltwater dammed by both ice and a newly formed moraine about 100 miles north of the park filled the western part of the Lake Superior basin. The enormous body of water is called Glacial Lake Duluth. With rising temperatures at the end of the ice age, the lake waters broke the deteriorating ice dam, and a tremendous flow of water and ice chunks overrode the moraine and coursed down the St. Croix River valley, which at the time was a wide, shallow valley lying in Cambrian sandstone.

The massive flood of ice water quickly eroded the sandstone, digging the valley deeper until it reached the more resistant

The modern St. Croix River is a small stream compared to the glacial flood that carved the Dalles through thick basalt.

basalt. The basalt layers were laced with joints, or vertical cracks, caused by the cooling of the lava. Roaring floodwaters flowed over and into these joints, widening them and breaking away chunks of basalt, thus chiseling the valley deeper. The river created the deep gorge in about 500 years, a very quick erosional event in terms of geologic time. Since then, winter frost has continued to pry basalt chunks loose, dropping them to talus piles on the river's edge. The sheer vertical walls created by water, ice, and frost attract 250,000 or more visitors to the park every year, including rock climbers.

Potholes drilled in basalt by floodwaters at Interstate Park. This pothole is about 4 feet in diameter and 7 feet deep.

The small pits in the basalt are vesicles. The photo spans 11 inches of basalt from top to bottom.

Within the eddies of the roaring glacial flood, sand, gravel, and rocks were pulled down in spirals and swirled rapidly against the streambed. Like natural drill bits, they made shallow circular depressions in the bedrock that became deeper with sustained grinding. The larger rocks caught in these maelstroms became rounded over time, some of them to nearly perfect spheres, and they in turn carved spiral patterns into the potholes. Geologists have found and studied many of these grindstones in the potholes of Interstate Park.

The park has the largest concentration and best examples of flood-produced potholes in the world. On the Wisconsin side, potholes up to 8 feet in diameter and as deep as 18 feet can be viewed from the Potholes Trail. (There are even larger potholes on the Minnesota side of the park.) Some of the potholes along the trail are more than 100 feet above the river, telling us that the glacial flood must have spanned the entire park for many decades. When the flood level finally dropped, the potholes we see today were left high on the rocky bluffs.

Basalt is uniformly fine-grained, so it is hard to distinguish individual lava flows. At Interstate Park, look for differences in coloration to identify layers. The upper part of a basalt layer can be lighter colored (dark brown as opposed to black) because the exposed part of any layer was weathered and oxidized for decades or centuries before the next flow of lava covered it. Another sign you are looking at the top of a flow is the presence of bubble-like and tube-like spaces, called *vesicles*. These spaces formed where gases or minerals less dense than the lava rose to the surface of a lava flow and were trapped as the lava cooled. If you are looking down at the top of a flow, such as at a flat stepping-stone or a horizontal expanse of basalt, you might see the tops of vesicles, which look like little pits. While many will be empty, some might be filled with white, pink, or green minerals, including quartz, plagioclase feldspar, and chlorite. The mineral-filled vesicles are called *amygdules*.

Sparse plant communities grow on basalt at Osceola Bedrock Glades.

10 OSCEOLA BEDROCK GLADES

Fragile Plant Community on Inhospitable Lava

The Osceola Bedrock Glades State Natural Area protects a fragile rare plant community. Although the glade is thinly vegetated, its plant community is well-developed and old—one of only four such communities in all of Wisconsin and not at all common elsewhere in the country. Hikers are strongly urged to stay on the trail to avoid damaging the rare ecosystem. To reach Riverview Trail, which takes you to the glade, find the parking area west of County Highway S (or River Road) just north of Osceola. Walking west on that trail, you pass through an oak woodland and onto an expansive, thinly vegetated, rocky exposure called a bedrock glade. A few yards beyond its western margin is the east rim of the St. Croix River valley, with views of the broad floodplain and its lakes and wetlands.

The Osceola Bedrock Glades is an exposure of bedrock basalt, formed from lava that erupted from the Midcontinent Rift around 1.1 billion years ago. The bedrock was scoured clean of soil by erosion, so there are little to no nutrients available for plants. The plant species in the glade evolved to withstand harsh conditions with limited water and little or no soil. Lichens and certain mosses, ferns, and fungi grow here, and low-growing herbs and shrubs can also take hold. Any trees that become established are stunted—thin and gnarly compared to the same species growing in good soil.

11 WILLOW RIVER STATE PARK

Waterfalls over Dolomite Ledges

The Willow River flows east and southeast for 61 miles across St. Croix County to the St. Croix River on Wisconsin's western border. Most of the Willow River's length lies within Early Ordovician bedrock of the Prairie du Chien Group, named after a Wisconsin town on the Mississippi River. The lowermost part of this group is the Oneota Dolomite—140 feet of resistant carbonate rock. The Willow River flows over broad ledges of the dolomite at Willow Falls, a spectacular cascade through a short canyon and a popular destination for people from nearby Hudson and from the Twin Cities of Minneapolis and St. Paul, just across the St. Croix River in Minnesota.

The sedimentary rocks of the Prairie du Chien Group were deposited in shallow, quiet water off the coast of an Ordovician sea that slowly advanced over the area. The Oneota Dolomite, its lowest and largest formation, contains dolomitic quartz sandstone and sandy dolomite, reflecting the deepening of the seawater as the shoreline moved inland. Thus, from bottom to top, the formation becomes progressively less sandy and more purely dolomitic. The buff-colored, massive canyon walls overlooking Willow Falls are typical of this group. It contains oolites—sand grains and other particles sheathed in silica that was precipitated from the Ordovician seawater.

The upper body of the Prairie du Chien Group is the Shakopee Formation, the lowest member of which is the New Richmond Sandstone, named for a city upstream on the Willow River. The sand was deposited along the shore when the sea advanced again. As the sea deepened, a 45-foot-thick layer of dolomitic rock was deposited over the thin layer of sandstone. It is called the Willow River Dolomite, named for its exposure along Willow River. Similar to the Oneota Dolomite, it contains interbedded sandy and oolitic dolomites with nodules of chert and gray-green shale. The small cavities in the canyon walls formed as groundwater dissolved the lime in the rock.

Oolites in the Oneota Dolomite. Sample is 4 inches long. —Specimen in the collection of the University of Wisconsin Geology Museum

Willow Falls cascades over ledges of dolomite.

Willow Falls lies on the east side of Willow River State Park. From the falls, the river flows southeast and was dammed close to the west side of the park to form Little Falls Lake, a popular place for boating and swimming. In 2015, the dam was removed due to safety concerns. (As of 2018, the plan is to build a new dam and refill the lake.) Just downstream from the dam site on the west side of the river is a prominent exposure of Cambrian sandstone. It was raised up 300 to 400 feet above the younger Ordovician dolomite to the east by the Hudson Fault. The sandstone contains fossils of trilobites, hyolithids, and brachiopods that lived here at the bottom of the Cambrian sea some 500 million years ago.

12 ROCK ELM DISTURBANCE

A Meteor Impact Crater

In northwestern Wisconsin, the terrain lying within St. Croix, Dunn, Pierce, and Pepin Counties resembles the state's famous Driftless Area, just to the south, with its prominent ridges, hills, hollows, and valleys. Although early glaciers covered these counties, the ice sheet of the most recent glaciation did not, so the area avoided the massive glacial erosion that affected most of the rest of Wisconsin. Despite its hilly appearance, the layers of rock underlying it are mostly flat—dolomite of the Prairie du Chien Group deposited on Cambrian sandstone—and have been left largely undisturbed for hundreds of millions of years.

In southeastern Pierce County, however, the bedrock below the thin layer of older glacial till lacks the predictable horizontal rock layering that defines the surrounding area. A roughly circular area nearly 4 miles in diameter is rimmed by a raised, segmented fault zone along which the dolomite bedrock is folded and fractured, with chunks of it tilted almost to vertical. Inside this zone is a roughly concentric zone of shale and sandstone not found anywhere else in this part of the state. At the center of the circular area is a dome made of a type of sandstone normally found hundreds of feet below the surface.

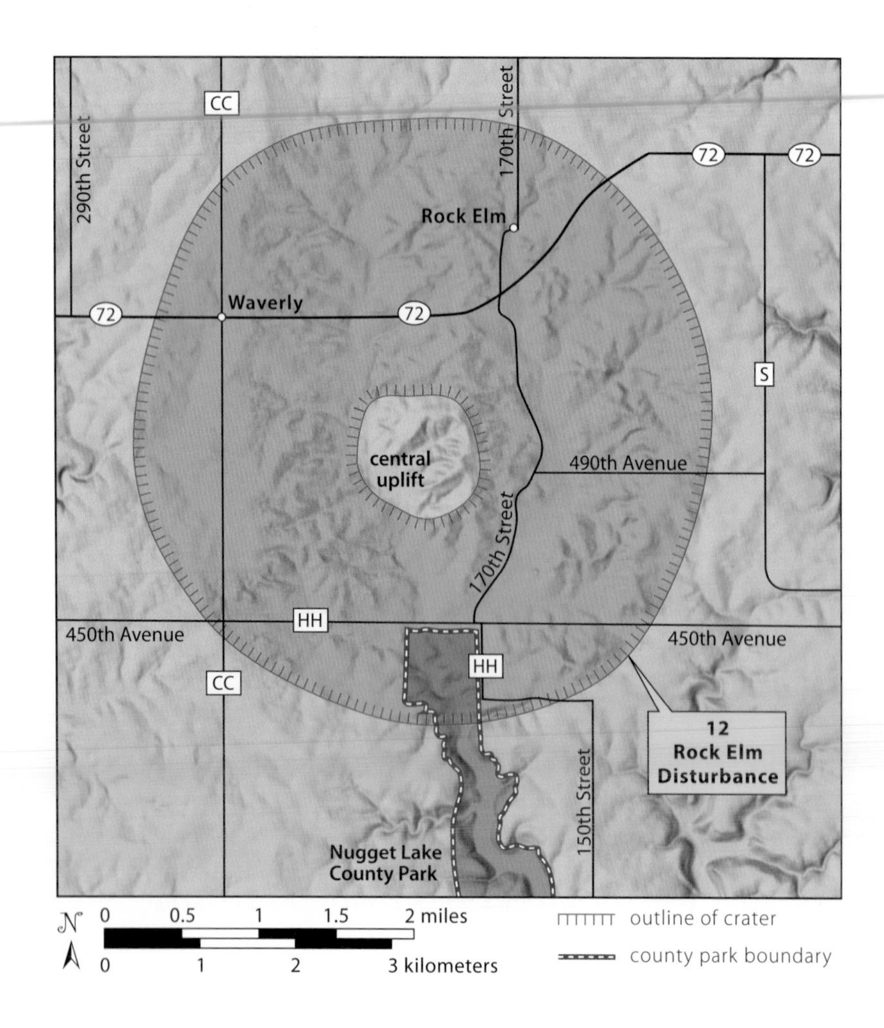

Prairie du Chien dolomite overlying Cambrian sandstone, the typical flat-lying sequence of rocks in much of northwestern Wisconsin.

Geologists named the unusual structure the Rock Elm Disturbance for the small town located within it. Researchers considered a number of possible hypotheses to explain the disturbance, including a burst of pressurized gas or water from below, but they have settled on a meteor strike as the most likely explanation. A shallow sea covered the region when the meteor struck about 470 million years ago in Ordovician time, not long after the deposition of the Prairie du Chien dolomites. Scientists estimate the meteor was 560 feet in diameter and traveling at 67,000 miles per hour when it hit, blasting a hole nearly 4,000 feet deep and 4 miles across on the seafloor. With the explosive energy of 63,000 Hiroshima-sized atomic bombs, the blast would have vaporized much of the seawater and flattened everything within 45 miles of its center.

Following the explosion, the central area of the crater rebounded, pulling up rock from deep below to form a dome. Called a *central uplift*, this feature has been noted in craters on the moon and other celestial bodies. The Rock Elm crater and its central dome would have been well defined shortly after the collision, but since then the deposition of more sediments by ancient seas, hundreds of millions of years of erosion, and scouring by the Pleistocene ice sheets have obscured it. However, it is still faintly visible on satellite photos and topographic maps.

Geologists first noticed that a zone of fractured bedrock around the ancient crater's rim, especially on its southern segment, had dropped as much as 150 feet from its normal position. These pieces of bedrock endured the blast and slumped into the crater, some of them tilting to nearly vertical. Most of the tilted bedrock has been buried by sediments, but a prominent example unearthed by erosion is Blue Rock, a downward fold created by the meteor strike. The folded dolomite is exposed on the bank of Plum Creek, accessible on a trail in Nugget Lake County Park, off County Highway HH, about 15 miles east of Ellsworth.

The central uplift, an oval-shaped range of hills up to 1.5 miles across, reaches as high as 200 feet above the surrounding land. The hills are made largely of late Cambrian Mt. Simon Sandstone, at least 500 million years old. This coarse quartz sandstone dips 22 to 44 degrees outward from the center of the uplift. These tilted slabs originated from 600 to 800 feet below the surface, where this type of stone normally lies in flat beds. Also found within the central uplift are fragments of granite, quartzite, chert, and sandstone, some of which are encased within a glassy material thought to be sandstone melted by the blast of the meteor impact. Researchers also found reidite, a rare mineral that was converted from zircon by the heat and

Tilted layers at Blue Rock along Plum Creek in Nugget Lake County Park.

Rock Elm Shale, exposed in an old quarry off 490th Avenue north of Nugget Lake County Park, is the mud that filled the meteor crater.

pressure of the blast. Reidite has been found in just three other meteor impact sites.

Shortly after the collision, a slurry of seawater, mud, and pulverized rock blown up and out from the center sloshed back into the crater. Known as basin fill, the sediment includes the 90-foot-thick Rock Elm Shale—a group of gray, green, and brown shales interbedded with fine-grained, silty feldspar-rich sandstone. Overlying this layer in the basin fill is Washington Road Sandstone—about 40 feet of white to buff-colored, fine-grained feldspar-rich sandstone. Both rocks are Middle Ordovician, estimated to be 472 to 461 million years old, whereas the bedrock surrounding the impact structure is Early Ordovician, the 500-to-480-million-year-old Prairie du Chien Group.

The Rock Elm Disturbance is one of five impact sites of similar age lying in a roughly straight line between Ames, Oklahoma, and the Slate Islands in northern Lake Superior. Another crater lies east of this line at Glover Bluff near Coloma, Wisconsin. Some astronomers have proposed that they were all created when a collision in the asteroid belt some 469 million years ago sent a barrage of asteroid fragments hurtling toward Earth. Or did a massive asteroid explode upon hitting Earth's atmosphere and pepper the planet with large meteorites? There are currently no scientific tools that allow us to know for certain, but the ideas are intriguing.

The first geologist to map the Rock Elm Disturbance, William S. Cordua of the University of Wisconsin–River Falls, cowrote a geology tour guide for the site. It tells the compelling story of the Rock Elm Disturbance and includes a walking tour to Blue Rock and other notable features within Nugget Lake County Park, as well as a driving tour that takes visitors to a vista looking into the ancient crater from its south rim.

13 BIG FALLS COUNTY PARK

Banded Gneiss of the Canadian Shield

Central Wisconsin lies near the southern edge of the Canadian Shield—the ancient rocks that form the core of present-day North America. The Chippewa River and its tributaries have cut through the glacial till and younger rock layers to expose the Precambrian rock in several places. One such location is Big Falls on the Eau Claire River east of Altoona, accessed off County Highway Q (Olson Drive) on the north side of the river. The rock here, which is exposed along the river from about 2 miles upstream of the falls to 2.5 miles downstream, is thought to have been originally an igneous intrusion that metamorphosed the country rock and was later metamorphosed itself. Four distinct rock units are found here, all of which appear together only at the falls: a banded amphibolite gneiss with alternating dark hornblende-rich and light plagioclase-rich bands; a dark green to black finely banded amphibolite schist; anorthosite, a visibly crystalline rock formed deep in the Earth's crust; and a metamorphic rock in transition between the amphibolite schist and the anorthosite. The latter three units are best exposed on the island in the falls, more accessible when the river is running low.

The extremely complex geologic history of these rocks is challenging for researchers to decipher. It is difficult to tell which rocks are the original igneous intrusive rocks and which rocks were metamorphosed by the intrusion or deformed after the intrusion. However, researchers have concluded that much of this rock was folded, faulted, and recrystallized during three separate periods of metamorphism. The first occurred in Archean time, more than 2,500 million years ago. The second occurred in Proterozoic time during the Penokean mountain building episode around 1,850 million years ago. And the third probably happened during a lower-grade metamorphic period that affected much of the Lake Superior region around 1,700 million years ago, possibly as a result of a collision with another primitive continent to the south.

The base of the oldest Cambrian rock in this area, the Mt. Simon Sandstone, is exposed in the walls of the shallow gorge around Big Falls.

Precambrian amphibolite schist at Big Falls.

Big Falls drops over banded Precambrian gneiss.

IRVINE PARK AND MT. SIMON PARK

Cambrian Sandstone atop Precambrian Gneiss

In west-central Wisconsin, exposures of Precambrian rock of the Canadian Shield are rare. To the north and east, the Precambrian bedrock lies under deepening glacial deposits. To the southwest, the Precambrian rock dips at 10 feet per mile beneath thickening layers of Paleozoic sandstones, shale, and other sedimentary rock. The contact between the Precambrian rock and overlying Cambrian sandstone is only exposed in a few places, including Irvine Park on the north side of Chippewa Falls.

In the east-central part of Irvine Park, look for the contact on the east bank of Duncan Creek about 50 yards north of where Bear Den Road crosses the creek on a bridge closed to car traffic. Hike along the east side of the stream north of the bridge to find the site. Below the sandstone lies weathered Precambrian gneiss, a medium-grained, metamorphosed granitic rock composed mostly of plagioclase, quartz, and biotite. The granitic magma originally intruded the Canadian Shield about 1,850 million years ago, then was converted to gneiss by metamorphism. For hundreds of millions of years prior to the deposition of sands, the Precambrian gneiss was exposed to erosion and weathering, which converted the upper part to a saprolite, a soft rock rich in clay minerals, especially kaolinite. The continent was south of the equator at the time with humid, tropical conditions favorable to the formation of kaolin-rich clay. At Irvine Park the gray-green saprolite layer is 6 to 10 feet thick.

About 530 million years ago, a Cambrian sea advanced from the southeast. Broad, braided streams flowing to the seashore brought sand and silt from the disintegrating granites and quartzites to the north, depositing what became the lower layers of the Mt. Simon Sandstone. As the sea continued to deepen, fast-flowing tidal currents deposited more layers of the sand. The Mt. Simon Sandstone is divided into three units: a thick-bedded, coarse-grained pebbly lower unit, a coarse- to medium-grained middle unit, and an upper unit of thinner-bedded, coarse- to very-fine-grained sandstone. Above the saprolite at Irvine Park, the lower unit of Mt. Simon Sandstone and about 10 feet of the middle unit are exposed in the 60-foot-tall outcropping.

Mt. Simon Sandstone is named for a major outcrop in Mt. Simon Park in north-central Eau Claire, about 10 miles southwest of Irvine Park. It stands 80 feet over the Chippewa River and represents the complete set of rock units making up Mt. Simon Sandstone. The Precambrian rock beneath it is not exposed here.

At Irvine Park, Mt. Simon Sandstone overlies Precambrian gneiss that was converted to saprolite.

You can still see grains of gneiss in the weathered saprolite.

Mt. Simon Sandstone at Mt. Simon Park in Eau Claire.

A kettle lake at Chippewa Moraine State Recreation Area.

15 CHIPPEWA MORAINE STATE RECREATION AREA

Topographic Reversals Created Kettles and Ice-Walled Lake Plains

The Chippewa Lobe of the continental ice sheet moved into northwestern Wisconsin from the north-northeast and built its terminal moraine across Chippewa County. Lying across a segment of this moraine is the Chippewa Moraine State Recreation Area, located 7 miles east of WI 53 (6 miles east of New Auburn) on County Highway M. The moraine at this point is a little over 5 miles wide, although it is twice that width along much of its length. Within the borders of the recreation area are some of the best-preserved examples in the world of topography that forms in the wake of continental glaciation.

The Chippewa Moraine is a classic example of a dead-ice moraine, created by a band of large chunks of ice that were separated from the main body of the glacier late in its life, between 11,000 and 10,000 years ago. Unlike the moving glacial ice, this stagnant ice remained stationary and became mostly covered by glacial debris carried by meltwater flowing away from the active ice margin. The stranded and stagnant ice was about 150 feet thick and melted at a rate of a few inches per century. The debris in and on the ice settled in uneven depths, creating hummocky topography that varies in height by 20 to 100 feet throughout the moraine.

Another topographic feature that speaks of this region's glacial past is the kettle, a pot-shaped depression on the land surface that had been occupied by a large chunk of buried ice. When these blocks of "dead ice" finally melted away, decades or even centuries after being separated from the glacial margin, many of their depressions were filled with water and became lakes and wetlands. Close to 15,000 kettle lakes dot the Wisconsin landscape. Kettles are an example of topographic reversal—when an elevated area (the buried ice) becomes a depression after the ice melts.

On the stagnating ice sheet at the end of the Wisconsin glaciation, some pockets of ice melted down to bare ground or close to it, becoming depressions in the ice that filled with meltwater. These ice-walled lakes typically sat for centuries, collecting sediments that settled to the bottom. The mostly flat lake bottoms built up over the years within the surrounding ice walls. The heavier, more gravelly sediments flowing off the ice settled near the lakeshores, and the more silty sediments settled across the lake floor interiors. When the surrounding ice finally melted away, what was left behind was a raised, roughly circular flat bed of silt with a gravelly low rim around it. The land around this area typically sloped away, and because of topographic reversal what had long been a flat lake floor was now a flat-topped hill, called an ice-walled lake plain. Some are more than 1 mile in diameter, and because of their rich silty soil, many have been converted to farm fields. The recreation area has preserved a number of ice-walled lake plains, including the one on which the David R. Obey Ice Age Interpretive Center now sits.

The Interpretive Center contains a rich collection of information and visual displays that explain glacial dynamics in general and the Chippewa Moraine in particular, and it commands good views of surrounding glacial landforms. A total of 23 miles of hiking trails, including a segment of the Ice Age National Scenic Trail, wind from the Interpretive Center down into the deeply wooded hummocky terrain.

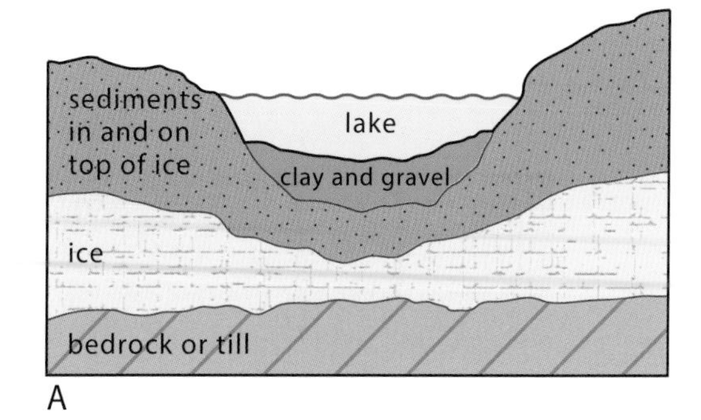

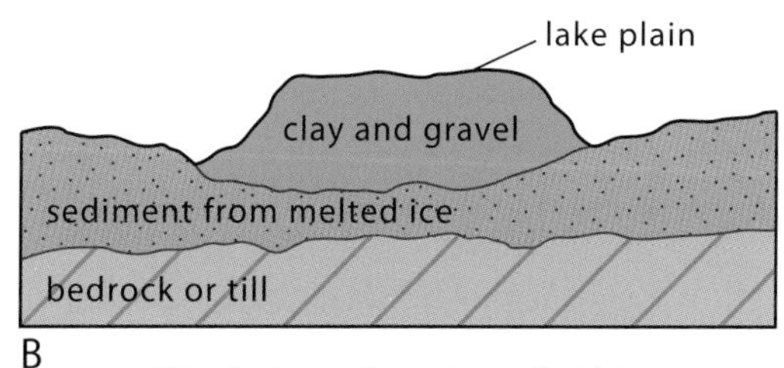

After the ice melts, an ice-walled lake plain becomes a flat-topped hill.

The David R. Obey Ice Age Interpretive Center was built on an ice-walled lake plain.

16 DELLS OF THE EAU CLAIRE COUNTY PARK

Precambrian Rhyolite Polished by Meltwater

The Eau Claire River of north-central Wisconsin, not to be confused with another Eau Claire River that flows through the city of Eau Claire, enters the Wisconsin River near Wausau. About 14 miles east of Wausau, the river drops 65 feet within a half mile stretch through the Dells of the Eau Claire County Park, crossing upended and exposed layers of Precambrian metamorphosed rhyolite, a volcanic rock.

The reddish rhyolite was metamorphosed to schist during the Penokean mountain-building episode about 1,850 million years ago. The schist here is flanked on the east and west (upstream and downstream, respectively) by bodies of granitic rock and gneiss. Small almandine (garnet) grains are abundant in the gneiss. In some places, the rock layers were tilted to a nearly vertical orientation, which enabled them to split more easily along cleavage planes. Where the river crosses such planes, rapids and waterfalls have formed.

During the Quaternary Period, the park area was covered by glaciers at various times but not by the most recent ice sheet—the Wisconsin glaciation. The park is surrounded by hummocky glacial terrain, but the glacial sediments are thin compared to more recently glaciated areas. The sediments are thought to be around 130,000 years old. Meltwater from all the glaciations, including the most recent one, gushed through the gorge, each flow cutting it a little deeper. Meltwater probably collected on the broad expanse of land to the east, known as Antigo Flats, and then funneled through the dells.

The flat slabs of rock on which swimmers now lounge on hot summer days were scratched and polished by glacial ice and centuries of meltwater flow. The floods of churning meltwater also eroded potholes in the rock. Stones and sand grains were caught in eddies and whirled intensely against the rock surfaces for centuries, boring these kettle-shaped depressions.

The park hosts a well-preserved stand of northern mesic forest, with hemlock, sugar maple, yellow birch, mountain maple, and Canada yew. Several short trails wind through the park, including a 2.6-mile stretch of the Ice Age National Scenic Trail. In 1973, a large section of the park was designated as a state natural area with the intention of preserving its unique geologic and biological features.

Glacial meltwater polished and carved potholes into this exposure of rhyolite. —Courtesy of John Luczaj

Waterfalls and pools at the Dells of the Eau Claire County Park attract thousands of visitors every year.

These lines formed by differential weathering of the shear zones in the metamorphic rhyolite. You can easily distinguish them from glacial striations because the shear lines are not parallel to each other and here are oriented perpendicular to the direction of ice movement. Glacial striations, on the other hand, would be parallel and would show that the ice moved from the northeast toward the southwest.

17 RIB MOUNTAIN STATE PARK

A Quartzite Monadnock

Rib Mountain, located just southwest of Wausau and close to the geographic center of Wisconsin, is a prominent example of a monadnock—an isolated peak standing above a plain created by a long period of erosion. The mountain, named for its slightly curved riblike shape, is a 4-mile-long ridge that is as much as 1 mile wide. Its highest point is 760 feet above the surrounding plain. Once known as Rib Hill, the official name was changed in 1949 to attract tourists to the area.

The upper portion of Rib Mountain is a mass of nearly pure quartzite, one of the hardest types of rock on the planet. It resisted hundreds of millions of years of erosion by wind, water, frost, and ice, while the land around it was beveled downward. While it is the fourth-highest point in Wisconsin, Rib Mountain is the highest exposure of bedrock in the state. Nearby are two other quartzite monadnocks—Mosinee Hill to the southeast and Hardwood Hill to the west—but both are much smaller than Rib Mountain.

The quartzite on these hills is made of sand eroded from the Penokean Mountains, consolidated into sandstone, and then metamorphosed during another mountain building episode around 1,700 million years ago. Some slabs of quartzite feature ripple marks, which indicate that the well-sorted sand was deposited near the shore of a sea. The ripple marks were preserved when a younger layer of sand covered them. Geologists think this quartzite was probably formed at the same time as other quartzite formations in the state, including the Baraboo Hills.

Around 1,450 million years ago, magma moved into rock beneath the surface in a large area to the east of Rib Mountain, creating a massive intrusion of granite known as the Wolf River Batholith. Geologists think this was part of a widespread igneous event because they have found granites and rhyolites of a similar age at sites from Missouri to Colorado and Arizona. Because there were no known tectonic plate collisions at this time, the cause of this widespread event is unknown.

The Wolf River intrusion created a row of volcanoes that were roughly centered where Rib Mountain is now. However, contrary to one popular notion, Rib Mountain and its neighboring monadnocks are not remnants of ancient volcanoes. Rather, a ring-shaped intrusion of syenite, a granular igneous rock composed largely of alkali feldspar, formed beneath one of the volcanoes and incorporated large and small chunks of

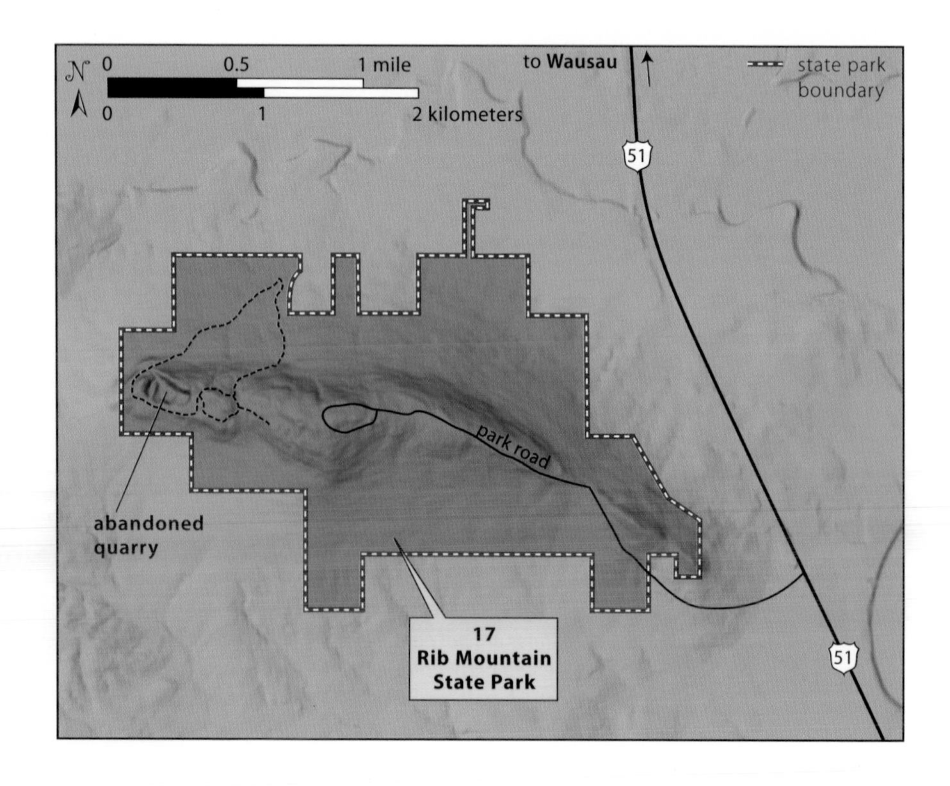

A quartzite mass called the Sphinx forms the high point atop Rib Mountain.

The wall of an abandoned quarry on Rib Mountain.

Upended layers of quartzite near the top of Rib Mountain.

quartzite into itself. Some of these layered bodies of quartzite were tilted to nearly vertical positions as they were heaved up, and these tilted layers are now visible on Rib Mountain.

Syenite erodes more readily than quartzite, so over hundreds of millions of years the volcanoes eroded away leaving the quartzite monadnocks as fragments of the ring-shaped intrusion. The quartzite protected the syenite beneath it, which is now exposed at the bases of all three hills. After Cambrian time, seas invaded the Wisconsin area several times, depositing sandstone and limestone layers that buried the quartzite monadnocks and eroded away time and again, leaving the quartzite peaks in place. In the Quaternary Period, glaciers also engulfed these hills several times, although not during the most recent Wisconsin glaciation.

In 1929, Rib Mountain State Park was established to protect the hill, a part of which beyond the park boundaries was quarried until 1990, when the park acquired the mined area. Trails in the park take hikers past many remarkable rock features and to the quarry, where the white-to-off-white quartzite is best exposed. From points on the trails, and from the park's 60-foot-tall observation tower, you can view the Hardwood and Mosinee Hills, Wausau, the Rib and Wisconsin Rivers, and glacial moraines to the north and east left by the Wisconsin glaciation. Also within park borders is a state natural area established to protect the sensitive talus forest community that includes a number of rare plant species. Hikers are asked to stay on trails to avoid disturbing this community, as well as to avoid injury in the park's extraordinarily rocky terrain.

18 MARINETTE COUNTY WATERFALLS

Flowing over Igneous Rocks of the Penokean Orogeny

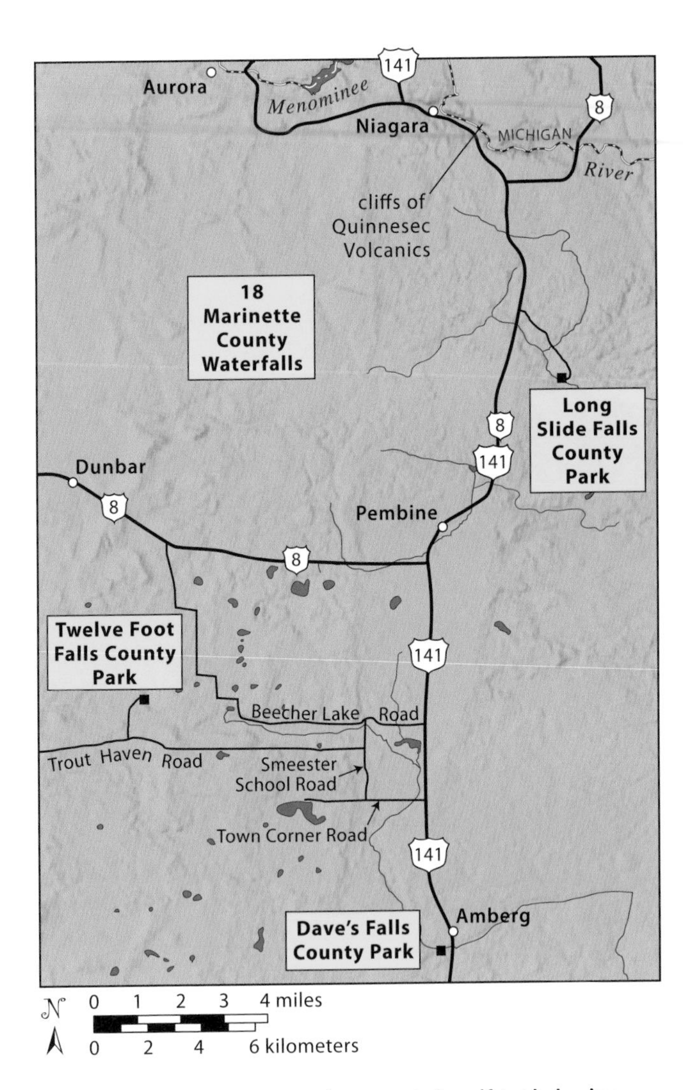

Marinette County managers have created a self-guided online tour of many more waterfalls than are shown here.

Marinette County is billed as the Waterfalls Capital of Wisconsin due to its twelve beautiful and accessible waterfalls and many more that are less accessible, lying in the deeper woods of this far northeastern county. Waterfalls often form due to a change in rock resistance, where a stream crosses from one rock type to another. In Marinette County, multiple fault zones caused by the Penokean Orogeny juxtapose many different rock types. Streams and rivers have cut through the area's thick layers of glacial till, exposing the bedrock along their banks and particularly at waterfalls.

Much of the bedrock is part of the ocean crust and volcanic islands that were mashed together and metamorphosed in the collision between the Superior and Marshfield continents—the orogeny that built the Penokean Mountains around 1,850 million years ago. One of the major components of the county's bedrock is the Quinnesec Volcanics, primarily dark-colored rock of former ocean crust, including greenstones, fine-grained basaltic rock, and metamorphosed gabbro, a coarse-grained intrusive rock sometimes called "black granite." Magma intruded the metamorphosed volcanic and sedimentary rock, adding granitic rock to the complex mosaic. A pink granitic rock, called Athelstane Quartz Monzonite, intruded about 1,860 million years ago, and a younger gray granite, called Amberg Quartz Monzonite, intruded about 1,650 million years ago.

The margin where the Superior and Marshfield continents collided, called the Niagara Fault, trends east and west just north of Marinette County. It is named for the town of Niagara on the Menominee River, which serves as the boundary between Wisconsin and the Upper Peninsula of Michigan. The ancient Superior continent lies north of the fault, and the belt of diverse Penokean rock types that make up most of Marinette County's bedrock lies to the south. From US 141 in Niagara, you can look across the Menominee River to get stunning views of cliffs of Quinnesec Volcanics, tilted up and sheared by the Niagara Fault.

You can see steeply tilted rock from the upper end of Long Slide Falls.

Cliffs on the Michigan side of the Menominee River, across from Niagara, expose Quinnesec Volcanics.

Three of the county's many spectacular waterfalls are described here. To reach Long Slide Falls from Niagara, travel south on US 141 about 7 miles to Morgan Park Road, which goes east, leading to Long Slide Road, which runs southeast to Long Slide Falls. Here the North Branch Peme bon Won River drops 50 feet within a fault zone in the Quinnesec Volcanics. Trails take you to vantage points at both the lower and upper ends of the cascade.

To reach Twelve Foot Falls County Park, head 4.5 miles south of Pembine on US 141 and turn west on Beecher Lake Road. In less than 2 miles, go south for less than 1 mile to Trout Haven Road and then west again another 6 miles. There the north branch of the Pike River flows in a fault zone over ledges of quartz diorite that is about 1,860 million years old.

Dave's Falls County Park is just south of Amberg where US 141 crosses the Pike River, which gushes through a deep, narrow gorge carved in the Athelstane (pink) and Amberg (gray) quartz monzonites. The top of the gorge displays excellent examples of glacially smoothed rock. The falls is named for a log driver who died in a logjam on the Pike River in the days when Wisconsin's pine forests were being cleared.

Dave's Falls.

EASTERN RIDGES AND LOWLANDS

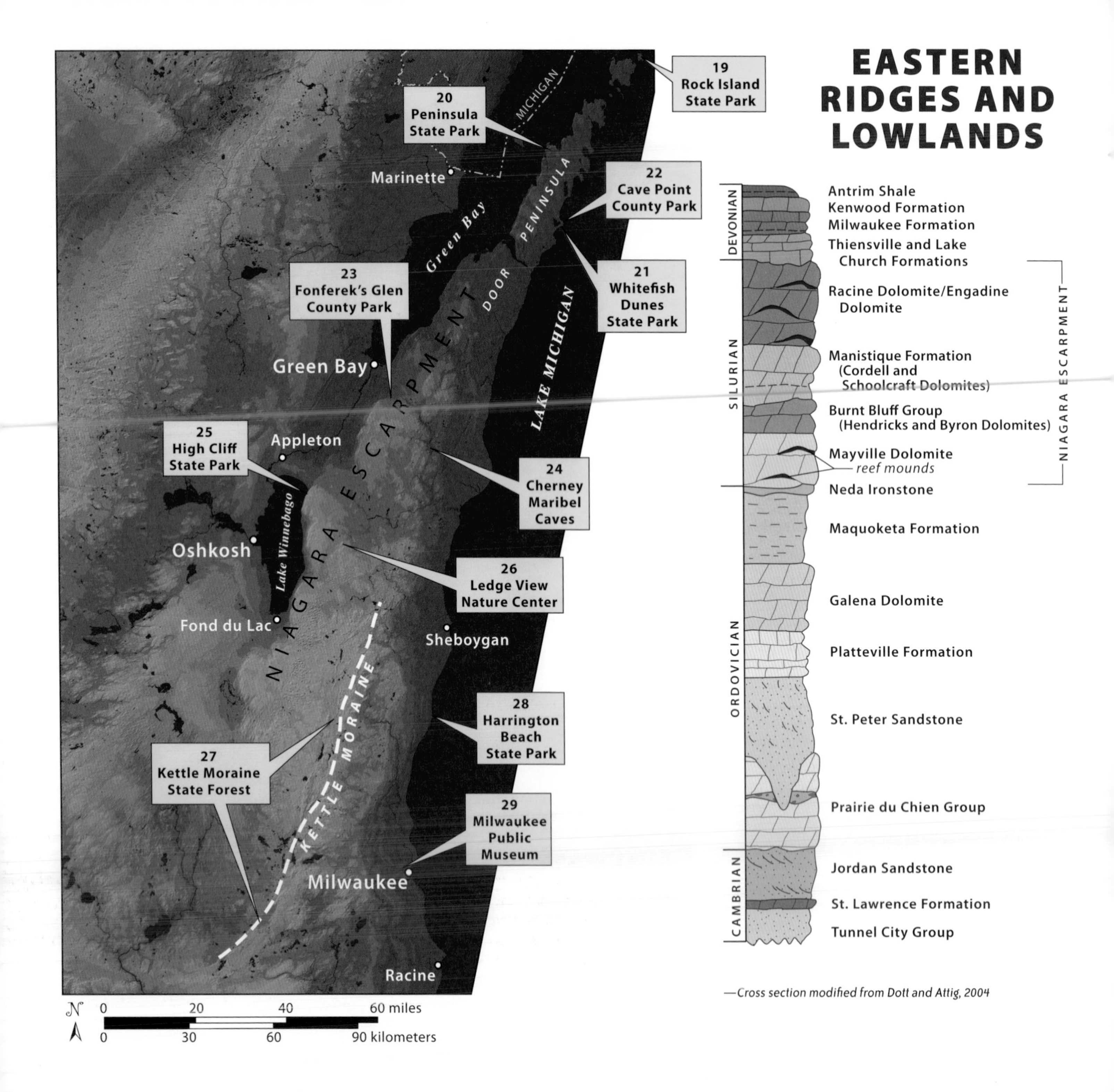

—Cross section modified from Dott and Attig, 2004

THE EASTERN RIDGES AND LOWLANDS

North-central Wisconsin is domed upward, and hundreds of millions of years of erosion scoured off the top layers of the dome, leaving it ringed with the ragged edges of underlying layers that dip radially away from the dome. Those edges of resistant rock layers form ridges, and the areas between them, where softer rock was carried away, are now lowlands. Thus the eastern half of the state is a province of ridges and lowlands. One of those ridges, the Niagara Escarpment, rises abruptly from the waters of Green Bay, which lies in one of the lowlands. The escarpment is the west side of a cuesta, the asymmetrical ridge that forms the backbone of the Door Peninsula. The cuesta stretches nearly 180 miles from southern Dodge County north through the peninsula to its outlying islands. It continues northeasterly through the mouth of Green Bay, follows the curving shore of Michigan's Upper Peninsula, then runs east and southeast through Ontario to its border with New York State. There, it forms the cliff that makes Niagara Falls, for which the escarpment is named.

The dolomite of the Niagara Escarpment—the most prominent ridge in the east—is a product of the Silurian seas, which lay over all or much of Wisconsin between 443 and 417 million years ago. These shallow, warm, and salty water bodies, much like today's Mediterranean Sea, hosted a rich diversity of lime-secreting organisms. The wastes and remains of these creatures accumulated on the seafloor, forming limestone that was later converted to dolostone, a rock type made mostly of the mineral dolomite. The rock dolostone is commonly referred to as dolomite.

Underlying the Silurian dolomites is the Maquoketa Formation of Ordovician age. The Niagara Escarpment exists because this thick, mostly shale formation eroded dramatically where exposed, especially during glaciation. Where the overlying dolomite remained intact, less erosion occurred. Because the layers dip down to the east, a cuesta formed where the layers meet, exposing the resistant dolomite cliffs and ledges of the Door Peninsula.

Inland seas deposited more layers of sedimentary rock in the Devonian Period, but little is known about what happened after the end of that period. Geologists refer to this time span—between about 400 and 2.6 million years ago—as a "lost interval," when erosion erased the record of whatever rocks may have been deposited. During the Wisconsin glaciation, the Green Bay and Lake Michigan Lobes covered all of eastern Wisconsin and played a dominant role in shaping this part of the state.

Pottawatomie Point, the highest shoreline cliff on Rock Island.

19 ROCK ISLAND STATE PARK

Niagara Escarpment Forms an Island in Lake Michigan

Rock Island, off the northeastern tip of the Door Peninsula, is part of a chain of several islands in the mouth of Green Bay. The archipelago is a deeply eroded stretch of the Niagara Escarpment that lies between the Door Peninsula and Michigan's Garden Peninsula. The gaps separating the islands were eroded by hundreds of millions of years of wind, rain, flowing water, and frost. The glaciers that inched across the land multiple times during the past 2.6 million years carved these gaps deeper.

Rock Island's west side rises steeply to as high as 140 feet above the water. The highest bluff, Pottawatomie Point on the island's northwest corner, is composed of Byron Dolomite, a white to light-gray, dense, very-fine-grained rock. Of all the island's rock formations, it is the most resistant to erosion. The bluff's name is derived from that of the region's most prominent native tribe, the Potawatomi.

Because it is part of the asymmetrical ridge of the cuesta, the island slopes gently east to the lower cliffs and beach area on its Lake Michigan side. The island is heavily wooded, although the forest soil is not deep. The Wisconsin glaciation left a thin layer of till with erratic boulders of granite and basalt. The sand spit on the southwest corner of the island has been formed by waves and currents working for thousands of years since the ice sheet departed, moving eroded sand from the island's shores as well as from the lake bottom.

Rock Island was probably used at least 2,000 years ago by Native Americans who camped on the island during summer months. After that, the Potawatomi and Ojibwe occupied the island, as well as European settlers who arrived in the late 1830s. The European population grew to more than two hundred by 1855, but by 1890 all surviving homesteaders had left the remote island for more populated areas to the south.

During the period of European settlement, ship traffic increased around the peninsula and through the narrow passages between the islands. Ships frequently wrecked on the dangerous shoals, so the US government established a series of lighthouses. The first of these was built on Pottawatomie Point in 1836 to light Rock Island Passage north of the island.

In 1958, it was replaced by a more sturdy structure, which now serves as a museum.

In 1910, the successful inventor and industrialist Chester Thordarson purchased most of Rock Island, finding that it reminded him of his native Iceland. He developed the southwest corner of the island and preserved the rest in its natural state. Using native stone—Byron Dolomite quarried from the peninsula and granite and rhyolite erratics dropped by the glaciers—he built several structures, including the impressive Viking Hall, designed to be a boathouse and meeting hall. It now serves as a museum that informs visitors about native cultures on the region's islands as well as about Thordarson's numerous achievements.

In 1964, Thordarson's heirs sold the island to the State of Wisconsin for use as a state park. No bikes or motorized vehicles are allowed in this primitive park, thus campgrounds are for tents only. The island is accessible by private boat and by a ferry service that operates in the spring, summer, and fall.

Thordarson's boathouse, known as Viking Hall, was built in the late 1920s from dolomite quarried from the Door Peninsula.

20 PENINSULA STATE PARK

Wave-Cut Caves in Dolomite Cliffs

Peninsula State Park, located on a prominent peninsula jutting north into Green Bay from the larger Door Peninsula, displays ancient shoreline features in Silurian dolomite of the Niagara Escarpment. The park's west-side cliffs expose the gray Mayville Dolomite, with weathered, thickly bedded, fine-to-medium-grained, cherty layers. In the park's central and western areas, the outcroppings are formed of the Burnt Bluff Group rock types, also commonly known as Niagara dolomite. The lower unit is Byron Dolomite—a white to bluish-gray, dense, fine-grained stone—and the upper unit is Hendricks Dolomite, which is buff to light brown and more coarse-grained than the Byron layers. The Byron Dolomite forms most of the dramatic cliffs, such as the 150-foot-tall Eagle Bluff overlooking Eagle Harbor.

In the millions of years prior to the Pleistocene glaciation, cracks formed in the dolomite layers covering the state. Streams draining the Door Peninsula flowed in the larger northwest-southeast-trending cracks and widened them through mechanical and chemical erosion. Beginning about 2.6 million years ago, the glaciers carved them even wider and deeper, and glacial meltwater roared through them. Two of the short streams that flow northwest off the Niagara Escarpment—Fish Creek and Ephraim Creek—created the valleys that today flank and define the smaller peninsula on which the state park sits.

The level of Lake Michigan changed in the centuries that followed the last glaciation. Two higher-level stages, known as Lake Algonquin and Lake Nipissing, lasted for several centuries each, the first around 11,000 years ago and the second around 5,000 years ago. Waves of each stage eroded terraces, ancient beaches, and caves along its shore, which lay inland from the present-day shore. Some of the park's hiking trails cross elongated bodies of cobblestones and boulders rounded by the ancient lake waves. Terraces line much of the shoreline of the park's peninsula, and the two towns on either side of the park—Fish Creek and Ephraim—each occupy such a terrace.

On the Eagle Trail in the park's northeast corner, hikers can see how caves form in the dolomite near the modern lake edge. Frost action and storm waves break the well-bedded rock into blocks that are gradually loosened, dismantled, and removed, leaving behind small angular caves. Eagle Cave, the bluff's most

Bluffs of Byron Dolomite tower over Eagle Harbor.

Eagle Cave was eroded by waves of an earlier version of Lake Michigan. Vertical joints and horizontal layering, or bedding, in the Byron Dolomite enables erosion to remove angular blocks.

famous opening, formed this way but is now 30 feet above the water level. The combination of the falling lake level and the land rebounding after the weight of the glaciers was removed has put this and other caves in Door County high above the lake.

Early Woodland Indians traveled through and established a village at the site of the park's Nicolet Bay Beach as early as 2,500 years ago. The area attracted European immigrant settlers and tourists beginning in the late 1800s. The lighthouse on Eagle Bluff was built in 1868 and is among the oldest surviving lighthouses in the Upper Midwest. Established in 1910, the state park is one of Wisconsin's oldest. In the 1930s, the Civilian Conservation Corps built trails, roads, buildings, and the Eagle Terrace Overlook—an impressive viewing platform on the site of an abandoned stone quarry.

21 WHITEFISH DUNES STATE PARK

A Former Sandbar

Whitefish Dunes separates Whitefish Bay on Lake Michigan from Clark Lake, an inland water body that was once part of a larger, deeper bay, the mouth of a southeast-flowing stream. After the Wisconsin glaciation, the level of Lake Michigan changed several times. About 5,000 years ago, a higher stage of the lake, called Lake Nipissing, filled the deep bay to a level perhaps 20 feet higher than it is today. The waves and currents of Lake Nipissing winnowed sand from the glacial deposits and built a sandbar running southwest from the dolomite headland, now called Cave Point, on the north side of the bay. Over the centuries, the sandbar grew, and when the level of Lake Nipissing dropped, the bar was exposed and continued to grow to the south. Eventually, it closed the mouth of the bay, isolating what is now Clark Lake from Lake Michigan.

Over thousands of years, the sandbar grew into a set of dunes, as wind took over for water as the major sculptor of what would become Whitefish Dunes. Water and wind move sand in much the same way. Water currents slow as they reach sandbars and drop the sediments they carry, adding to the sandbar. Winds carrying sand grains also slow when they encounter exposed sand and add to it by dropping sand grains. Hardy pioneer species such as marram grass became established on the shifting sand at Whitefish Dunes, and more plant species followed. Over time, these plant communities grew more complex, eventually becoming the dune forests you can see today.

About a half-mile wide and 1.5 miles long, Whitefish Dunes exhibits all the stages of dune formation, including newly forming dunes, tenuous dune grasslands, dune wetlands, conifer stands, and long-established dune forests. All of these ecosystems are fragile and, since 1967, have been protected as a state park. The trail to Old Baldy, the highest dune in the park, gives hikers a good sampling of the various stages of dune and dune forest formation. Visitors to the park can also view a replica of a Native American fishing village that was established between 1,100 and 1,200 years ago. Various native peoples have fished the waters of Whitefish Bay for more than 2,000 years.

Dunes forming at Whitefish Dunes State Park.

A honeycomb coral fossil (Favosites) from Whitefish Dunes State Park.

Wave-cut cliffs of Cordell Dolomite at Cave Point County Park.

22 CAVE POINT COUNTY PARK

Fossils in Wave-Cut Dolomite

This small county park, on the headland at the north end of Whitefish Dunes State Park, is known for its picturesque wave-cut caves and terraces on the Lake Michigan shore of the Door Peninsula. The bedrock on the sloping cuesta of the peninsula dips east, so the upper rock layers on the east side of the Door Peninsula are younger than those of the west side. Those of the east side belong to the Engadine Dolomite, the youngest of the Silurian dolomites, and the underlying Manistique Formation. The light-gray-to-white Engadine Dolomite is extremely dense, crystalline, and even-textured. It can also appear as a pinkish to purplish rock. Dissolution of the carbonate rock has enlarged its joints, or vertical cracks, into crevices and caves. The buff-colored Cordell Dolomite member of the Manistique Formation is the most widely exposed part of that formation on the peninsula, easily identified by its distinctively wavy bedding.

The Cordell Dolomite layers are very fossiliferous, often including pentamerid brachiopods (*Pentamerus*), stromatoporoids (fossil sponges), and corals, especially tubelike corals (*Syringopora*), chain corals (*Halysites*), and honeycomb corals (*Favosites*). Brachiopods resemble small clams but are not related to them (clams are bivalves). In the overlying Engadine Dolomite, fossils are less common but can contain sparse samples of brachiopods, snails, trilobites, and corals. Fossil viewing in the county park is popular, but fossil collecting is prohibited because the county park lies within the state park.

FONFEREK'S GLEN COUNTY PARK

Stone Arch in Cherty Dolomite

Bower Creek, which flows northerly across the east-west-trending section of the Niagara Escarpment, carved Fonferek's Glen, a deep, narrow canyon containing one of Wisconsin's few stone arches, or natural bridges. The upstream end of the glen is defined by a 30-foot waterfall. The glen lies in a 75-acre county park, located just over 4 miles south of the city of Green Bay off County Highway MM (Dutchman Road). A trail runs south along the west rim of the glen to the falls. When the creek is not too high, you can cross it upstream of the falls and take a path north through an abandoned quarry to its lower level and down to the creek bed on the east side of the gorge.

Fonferek's Glen, named for the family that formerly owned the land, lies in the Mayville Dolomite, which consists of three units within the glen: an upper 15-foot-thick unit of dense, resistant dolomite in clearly defined beds; a middle unit of about 15 feet of weaker, chert-rich dolomite, comparatively

Bower Creek flows over this ledge of resistant Mayville Dolomite when water is high. Flowing water has carved an alcove out of the cherty dolomite layer below the ledge.

A stone arch, or natural bridge, at Fonferek's Glen. All three units of the Mayville Dolomite are visible here: the well-bedded, resistant upper and lower units and the more easily eroded cherty unit in the middle.

more eroded; and a lower unit of well-bedded resistant dolomite containing some chert. All the layers are light brown and fine to medium grained and total about 54 feet in thickness. Fossils found here, mostly in the lowermost layer, include brachiopods, stromatoporoids (fossil sponges), and honeycomb corals (*Favosites*).

The cliffs and waterfall at Fonferek's Glen are among the few that exist because of the differential erosion of two dolomites of different resistance. Most waterfalls along the Niagara Escarpment occur because the dolomites overlie easily eroded shale of the Ordovician-age Maquoketa Formation. The resistant upper dolomite unit here forms both the ledge over which the water flows and the arch downstream. The Maquoketa Formation is exposed only in the creek bed in the form of soft greenish mudstone, but almost all of it is covered by talus—chunks of rock from the walls of the glen—and river sediments.

The stone arch in the glen is 40 feet high, 5 feet wide, and 5 feet thick, with a 14.5-foot span. It is a prime example of the mass wasting—the dislodgement and downslope movement of loosened rock and soil—that occurred following the most recent ice age. The middle layer of cherty dolomite was weakened by seeping groundwater and the regular expansion of water turning to ice in its crevices during cold periods. The eddy that formed at the sharp right bend in the creek downstream of the falls wore away at this weaker stone, further undercutting the more resistant dolomite ledge above and creating an alcove. At some point, the upper dolomite layer over the alcove collapsed along deep vertical cracks, called joints. Former landowner Norbert Fonferek reported to geologist Richard A. Paull that, in the mid-1950s, two horses strayed onto the overhang and broke through the thin roof of the alcove. The horses were rescued, but the opening remained, and erosion has since enlarged it. Erosion does not rest in the glen as frost, flowing water, and gravity continue to loosen blocks along joints.

24 CHERNEY MARIBEL CAVES

Meltwater Stream Exposes Solution Cavities

When the most recent glacier was retreating from northeastern Wisconsin beginning about 15,000 years ago, Glacial Lake Oshkosh formed in what is now the Green Bay–Fox River lowland just west of the Door Peninsula. As the ice melted and the lake rose, it found outlets to the east, flowing across the peninsula. Because the glacier retreated and advanced a number of times, the lake also formed and drained several times. Each time, an ice dam or fragile new moraine may have given way to the growing volume of lake water, quickly draining the lake. These rapidly flowing meltwater streams carved deep channels, carrying away softer rock and glacial till and leaving harder rock formations standing as cliffs.

The West Twin River flows southeast across the base of the Door Peninsula in one of these glacially carved channels in Manitowoc County. Just northeast of the village of Maribel, the fast-moving meltwater exposed caves in a long 30-to-60-foot-high cliff on the west side of the river. The caves are protected in Cherney Maribel Caves County Park on County Highway R, east of I-43, exit 164. Seven caves can be viewed daily, and two gated ones are opened only for scheduled tours led by volunteers from the Wisconsin Speleological Society. The caves are closed in winter to allow resident bats time for uninterrupted hibernation.

The caves are in Silurian dolomite that has eroded as karst, a type of topography formed when bedrock becomes laced with crevices, caves, and sinkholes. These solution features were chemically weathered out of the carbonate rock by slightly acidic water. Rainwater forms a weak carbonic acid solution when it absorbs carbon dioxide from the atmosphere and from soil and decaying organic matter on the ground. As it flows over limestone and dolomite, it gradually dissolves some of the

Ruins of Maribel Caves Health Resort, built from dolomite stone in the early 1900s.

Flowstone, stalactites, and ribbon stalactites forming inside New Hope Cave.

calcite, or calcium carbonate, contained in the rock. When the water table drops and caverns are exposed to air, calcite-laden water drips from the newly exposed cave ceilings, creating stalactites, stalagmites, and other formations, all called speleothems.

Geologists estimate the Maribel Caves to be several tens of millions of years old, based on the geologic history of the area. No materials have been found in the caves that would allow for radiometric dating, but glacial debris has been removed from several of the caves, indicating they pre-date the glaciations in Wisconsin. New Hope Cave, one of the caves that has been developed for touring, contains evidence of high-pressure water flow, probably a subglacial stream escaping from the weight of the ice by entering the cave system.

The many springs that seep or flow from beneath the rocks in the park remind us that the dolomite bedrock continues to be chemically eroded. The spring water has a high mineral content, which in the early 1900s inspired the building of the Maribel Caves Health Resort, a hotel and health spa, which went out of business in 1960. Nothing remains of the commercial operation except for the caves and springs for which it was known and the ruins of the old hotel.

Cave entrances at Cherney Maribel Caves County Park.

25 HIGH CLIFF STATE PARK

Lime Quarries above Lake Winnebago

A prominent section of the Niagara Escarpment frames the northeast shore of Lake Winnebago at High Cliff State Park. The 30-to-40-foot-high rock wall, known locally as the Ledge, overlooks the lake from the top of the steep ridge. East of the wall and 225 feet above the modern lake level sits a plateau, home to the eastern part of the state park and surrounding farmland. Even when Glacial Lake Oshkosh filled Green Bay and the Lake Winnebago lowland, the cliff stood high above the water. The water level of the glacial lake was as much as 65 feet higher than that of the modern lake.

The escarpment is made of hard Silurian dolomite, which overlies softer Ordovician shale of the Maquoketa Formation. The lowland containing Lake Winnebago is eroded into the shale. The ice sheets eroded the shale much faster than the dolomite, lowering the lake basin relative to the escarpment.

Three units of Silurian dolomite are present at the park. From the top down, they are the buff-colored-to-light-brown, coarse-grained Hendricks Dolomite; the bluish-gray, more dense and fine-grained Byron Dolomite; and the gray, more fossiliferous Mayville Dolomite. Exposed at the base of the cliffs is a reddish-brown clay, part of the Maquoketa Formation. All of these rock types became raw materials for European immigrants who developed the site beginning in the mid-1800s. They used the clay to make bricks. When it was played out, they quarried the

The dolomite palisades, known as the Ledge, at High Cliff State Park.

dolomite for building stone and to make lime. One company built large kilns near the lakeshore, then broke up and hauled the rock to the kilns to be heated for lime production. The lime was used as a soil additive and an ingredient of plaster and cement.

The quarrying went on for 60 years until the 23-foot layer of Hendricks Dolomite, considered to be the highest quality for making lime, was depleted. The Byron Dolomite, called "blue stone," was also quarried and hauled to the kilns. Modern-day fossil hunters might be dismayed to know that the lowest dolomite, the fossiliferous Mayville, was mostly crushed to make gravel. Before the quarrying boom was over in the mid-1950s, it supported the growth of a thriving town, called High Cliff.

In 1957, within a year after the last load of rock was baked in the kilns, the state opened High Cliff State Park. It preserves the remnants of the town and quarries, which are now being reclaimed by the forest. The park also protects nine effigy mounds built by Woodland Indians between AD 1000 and AD 1500 on the plateau near the cliff top. At least eighteen other mounds were destroyed by earlier farming or quarrying operations. In addition, the park includes a 125-acre state natural area, designated to protect the rare cliff ecosystem.

Dolomite rock layers that make up the ledge show bedding planes, joints, and cavities created by chemical erosion.

An abandoned quarry at High Cliff State Park.

26 LEDGE VIEW NATURE CENTER

Environmental Education, Caves, and a Quarry

The Ledge View Nature Center, located 8 miles east of Lake Winnebago and 2 miles south of Chilton off County Highway G (S. Madison St.), is perched on a high, rocky hill and commands views of the back side of the Niagara Escarpment to the west, locally known as the Ledge and hence the name of the center. Founded in 1978, the Ledge View Nature Center is part of the Calumet County park system and includes 105 acres of prairie and woods with 3 miles of trails. The outstanding environmental education facility provides well-researched, colorful displays on the geology and natural history of the area.

Ledge View lies on Silurian dolomite on the gently sloping east side of the Niagara Escarpment. Slightly acidic water slowly dissolved the dolomite layers at joints—vertical cracks in fractured bodies of dolomite—and at some contacts between layers, creating karst topography, or bedrock laced with caverns, crevices, and sinkholes. The park's three solution caves range in size from 30 to 35 feet deep and from 230 to 300 feet long. When discovered they were filled with glacial debris, which volunteers from the Wisconsin Speleological Society removed, bucket by bucket. Exploration of the caves involves some crawling, although there are a few large chambers within them.

An abandoned quarry on the west side of the hill, a short walk from the nature center, displays a spectacular wall of Silurian dolomite. The City of Chilton and Calumet County quarried and crushed stone here for road building in the 1920s and 1930s. Geologists estimate that each vertical inch of this stone represents about 300 years of deposition of the remains of algae, corals, sponges, snails, and other ancient sea life, all of which were converted to dolomite. The top of each layer indicates a temporary end of such deposition until a time when life could again flourish and lead to the buildup of another layer.

A trail leads to the quarry floor where you can study the wall. If you climb steps out of the quarry, you can take a short trail to the top of the wall. (Be very careful. The fence there is not meant for leaning or climbing, and it is a shear drop to the base of the wall.) This trail leads to an informative sign explaining the view. The high ridge to the east is the backside of the Niagara Escarpment. You are looking up the gentle 8-mile sloping side of the cuesta to the top of the escarpment, beyond which, hidden from view, is Lake Winnebago.

Dave's Sink, a sinkhole in Carolyn's Caverns. Note the rope used to reach the cavern floor. —Courtesy Al Schema, Wisconsin Speleological Society

The wall of an abandoned quarry at Ledge View Nature Center.
—Descriptions derived from a 2004 report by Joanne Kluessendorf and Donald G. Mikulic

The top 5 feet of rock belong to the Schoolcraft Member of the Manistique Formation of middle Silurian age, a brown, coarse-grained, and generally thick layered dolomite, which includes thin layers of chert near its midpoint. The sea under which this layer formed was probably deeper and less salty than earlier Silurian seas, allowing for a variety of primitive sea creatures to live.

This 5 feet of stone is the Hendricks Dolomite of the Burnt Bluff Group. It is white to bluish gray, very fine-grained, dense, and thinly layered, deposited in a shallow sea too salty for a wide variety of sea life.

The middle 20 feet of the Burnt Bluff Group is light brown, medium-grained, and medium-bedded dolomite, with a rougher texture than the layers above, that was deposited in a shallow, salty sea, similar to the Red Sea of today.

The bottom 5 feet, also of the Burnt Bluff Group, is Byron Dolomite—a bluish-gray, very dense, even-textured, thin-to-medium-bedded dolomite, formed under a shallow, salty sea.

27 KETTLE MORAINE STATE FOREST

Hummocky Topography Where Two Ice Lobes Met

The Green Bay and Lake Michigan Lobes covered the eastern part of Wisconsin during the most recent glaciation. They met along a north-south line, called an interlobate zone, where their collective debris now intermingles in a hummocky area called the Kettle Moraine. At a glacier's margin, melting ice drops its load of silt, sand, gravel, and boulders in an elongated pile called a moraine. An interlobate zone receives a double load because both conveyor belts of ice bring glacial debris to the moraine.

The Kettle Moraine—a complex highland stretching 120 miles from north to south—varies from 1 to 10 miles wide and sits 100 to 300 feet above the surrounding plain. A parallel set of ridges characterizes the northern interlobate zone and a single, more massive moraine forms the southern zone. By coincidence, the Kettle Moraine roughly parallels the Niagara Escarpment, mostly lying east of it because the Green Bay Lobe overrode the escarpment.

Most of the Kettle Moraine's material was locally derived, consisting largely of dolomite chipped from the underlying Silurian-age rock and pulverized into gravel and sand. Although the Kettle Moraine contains large proportions of finer

The Parnell Esker Trail, in the state forest's northern unit, follows the crest of a 2-mile-long esker in the Kettle Moraine. The trail leads to Parnell Tower, a 60-foot observation tower atop the highest point in the Kettle Moraine State Forest.

The Kettle Moraine formed at the juncture of the Green Bay and Lake Michigan Lobes.

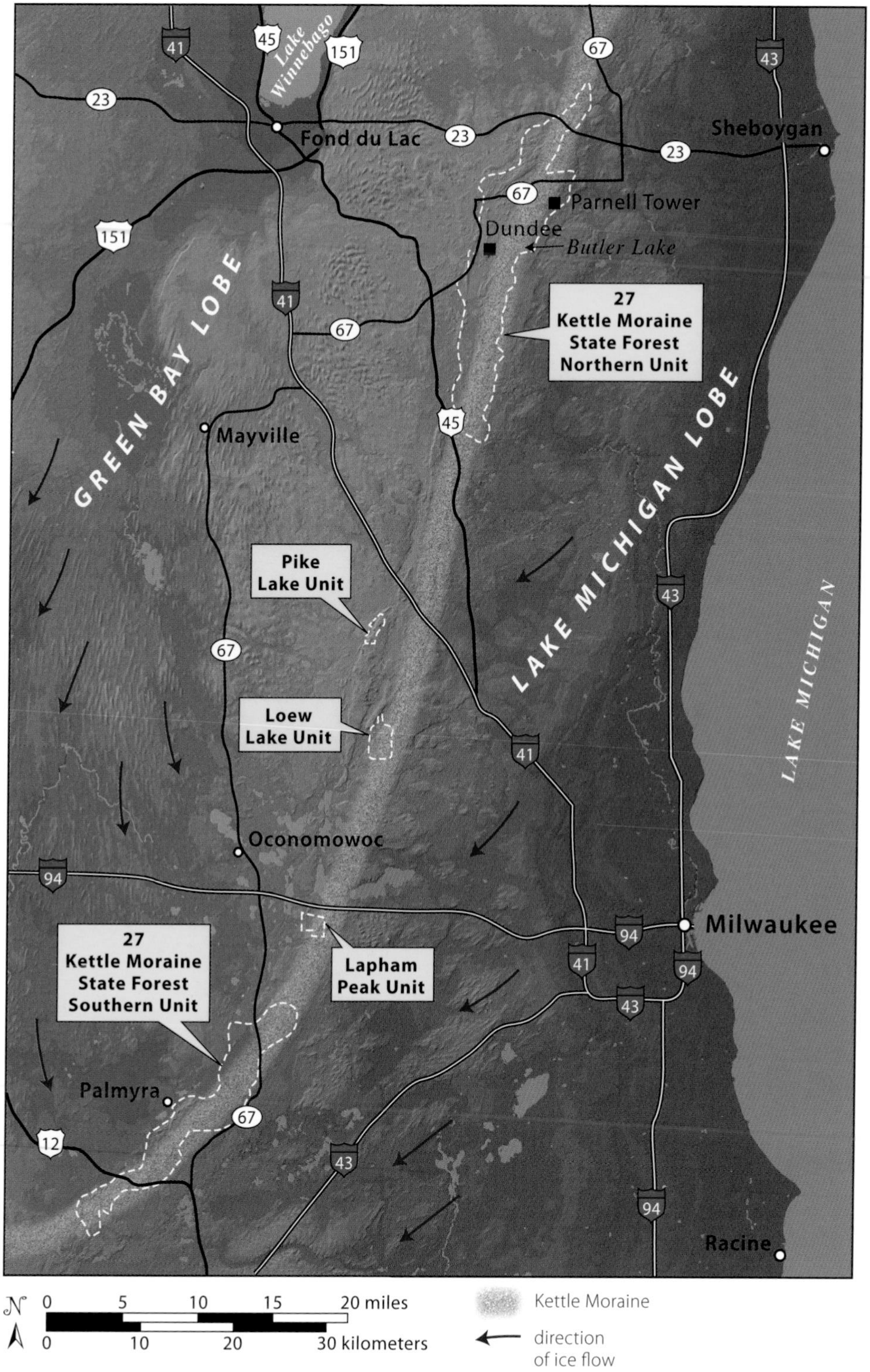

Dundee Mountain, a moulin kame in the Kettle Moraine, can be climbed via a winding trail.

Butler Lake, a small lake within a kettle peat bog, is east of Dundee in the northern unit of the state forest.

debris because streams running through the interlobate zone deposited silt, sand, and gravel, it has plenty of larger rocks and boulders—erratics carried by the glaciers from as far north as Canada.

The Kettle Moraine hosts a variety of glacially formed features, including its namesake—the kettle—a depression in the earth that was once occupied by a remnant body of ice. Large ice chunks were often buried by debris flowing from the glacier or blown by winds. Insulated by the debris, they often took decades or centuries to melt away. Kettles that drained completely and lie above the water table are now dry ravines or basins, but most contain water because they lie within or below the water table.

Fields of debris accumulated on top of the glacier, sometimes to depths of hundreds of feet, forming rolling landscapes on its surface. As the ice melted out, these fields of debris settled onto the land to become hummocky terrain—randomly arranged hills, or hummocks. Conical hills, known as moulin kames, or simply kames, are built of debris that flowed from the top of the glacier through vertical shafts, called moulins, that formed during melting. For centuries torrents of water dropped rocks, gravel, and sand down these shafts to pile up under the ice. Subglacial streams formed under the glacier, often running away from a kame, and these streams deposited debris along their subglacial channels. These linear deposits are now ridges, called eskers.

The hummocky terrain of Kettle Moraine State Forest provides pristine settings for study and enjoyment. Lapham Peak, a high hummock with a 45-foot observation tower, is a great place from which to view all these glacial landforms. Lapham Peak is named for Wisconsin's renowned early scientist Increase Lapham, who founded the National Weather Service and did pioneering work in weather observation from the peak.

The lake occupying an abandoned quarry at Harrington Beach State Park. The remains of the old elevator structure (visible in the foreground) used to take stone from the quarry are now submerged in the water.

28 HARRINGTON BEACH STATE PARK

Quarry in Fossiliferous Devonian Dolomite

At the end of the Silurian Period, the sea withdrew from the Wisconsin area, exposing the rocky land to erosion by wind, rain, and flowing water. Then, during the latter half of the Devonian Period, between 400 and 350 million years ago, another sea submerged all or most of Wisconsin, beginning a new round of deposition of sediments and the remains of sea creatures. Those deposits became layers of Devonian rock, almost all of which has since been eroded away in Wisconsin. The only rocks remaining lie in a narrow band along the southeastern shore of Lake Michigan, most of it covered by glacial deposits. One of few exposures is found at Harrington Beach State Park, on the shore of Lake Michigan, 37 miles north of Milwaukee. Within the park is an abandoned stone quarry filled by a 26-acre lake.

Devonian dolomite rims the quarry at Harrington Beach.

The top 10 feet of the rim rock of this quarry is dolomite of middle Devonian age, and a few feet of it are exposed above the water. Called the Lake Church Formation, it is the oldest of Wisconsin's Devonian exposures and is interspersed with thin layers of shale. The dolomite is light brown to gray, in contrast to the light-gray-to-whitish Silurian dolomite on which it was deposited (the contact being underwater in the quarry). This mostly thinly bedded, impure dolomite breaks apart easily into angular fragments. We know it is of Devonian age because the same type of rock was identified in Milwaukee in 1860 and was found to contain primitive fish fossils dating to the Devonian.

The Lake Shore Stone Company operated the quarry beginning in the late 1800s, furnishing crushed stone for the manufacture of lime and cement. Because the water table is high in this area, the quarrying operation required constant pumping, and when the quarry was abandoned in 1925 it quickly filled with water. Geologist Herding Cleland studied the quarry in 1911 before it was closed, providing a glimpse of what researchers saw there. He reported that the upper surface of the Devonian exposure was "finely smoothed and scratched by glacial action." The Devonian layers were rich in coral and gastropod fossils, and the lower 30 feet of the quarry walls was made of Silurian dolomite.

A small company town called Stonehaven occupied the site of the state park. Today, there are no signs of Stonehaven, although ruins of a structure used to move stone out of the quarry lie submerged on the east side of the quarry lake. A trail with informative signs circles the lake. The park also includes a sandy beach on Lake Michigan, and when the level of that lake is low, exposures of Devonian rock can be seen along its shore.

29 MILWAUKEE PUBLIC MUSEUM

Coral Reefs of Silurian Time

Corals were present in Ordovician time, but large reefs became established and flourished during the Silurian Period, which has been called the Age of Corals. At the time, North America was located on the equator and was largely covered by tropical seas. In Wisconsin, these seas were warm, clear, and shallow—probably not deeper than 200 feet—ideal for the development of coral reefs. More than once, Silurian seas filled the Michigan Basin, the broad lowland now occupied by Lake Michigan, the Lower Peninsula of Michigan, and Lake Huron.

Between 433 and 417 million years ago, reefs grew around the shallow margin of the basin. On its western side, they lived in a broad area stretching from northernmost Illinois and Indiana through Wisconsin and into southern Ontario, and from the lowland containing Green Bay and Lake Winnebago to a line east of the center of Lake Michigan. This area was dominated by tidal flats that were shallow north of Lake Winnebago and deeper to the south, which explains why the Wisconsin reefs thrived mostly in the southeast, especially between the present-day locations of Milwaukee and Racine.

Wisconsin's ancient reefs might have hosted more than two hundred species of sea life. These included spongelike stromatoporoids, tall flowerlike animals called crinoids, and shelled

A diorama of a Silurian reef in the Milwaukee Public Museum features clam-like creatures, trilobites, crinoids, cephalopods, and, of course, corals.

animals, including creeping snail-like gastropods, clinging brachiopods, and crawling trilobites. (The Wisconsin state fossil is *Calymene celebra*, a trilobite that lived on the reefs.) There might have been more than forty species of coral, including *Syringopora* (organ pipe corals), *Halysites* (chain corals), and *Favosites* (honeycomb corals), along with similarly interconnected colonies of structure-building bryozoans. The dominant predators on this seafloor were the long, octopus-like cephalopods.

While there are no easily accessible exposures of fossil reefs in Wisconsin, we can view a beautifully produced facsimile of an ancient reef in the Milwaukee Public Museum, at 800 West Wells Street in downtown Milwaukee. The museum also houses collections of local minerals and fossils from other periods, an excellent summary of the evolution of life-forms throughout Earth's eons, and an informative display on glaciers and how they affected Wisconsin.

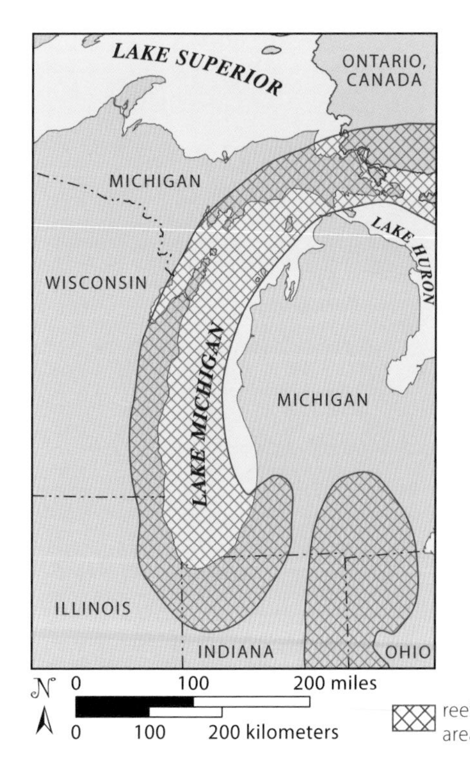

In Silurian time, coral reefs grew around the edge of the Michigan Basin.

Coral fossils from a Silurian reef. —Specimens on display at the Milwaukee Public Museum

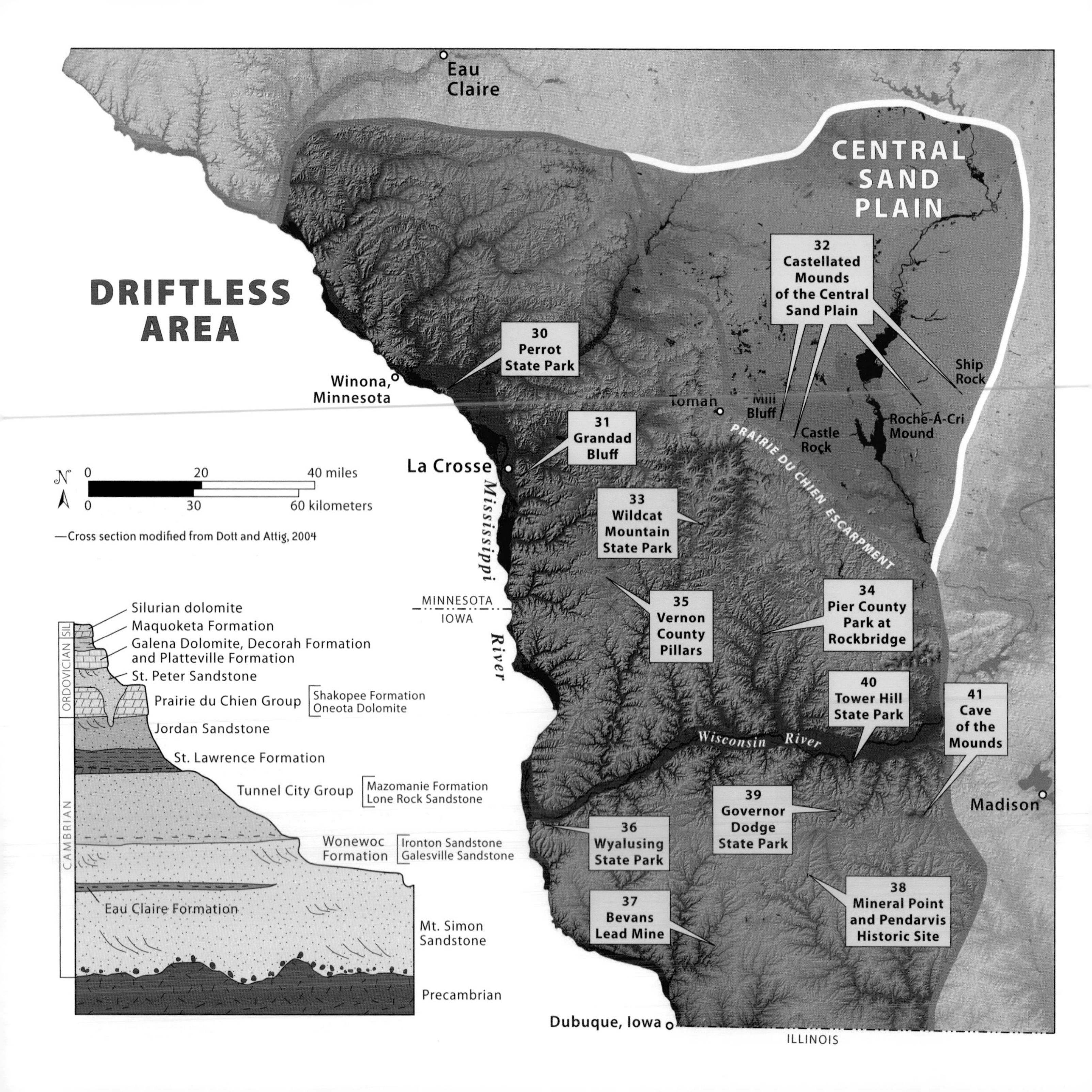

Eau Claire
CENTRAL SAND PLAIN
DRIFTLESS AREA
32 Castellated Mounds of the Central Sand Plain
30 Perrot State Park
Winona, Minnesota
Tomah
Mill Bluff
Castle Rock
Roche-A-Cri Mound
Ship Rock
31 Grandad Bluff
La Crosse
PRAIRIE DU CHIEN ESCARPMENT
0 20 40 miles
0 30 60 kilometers
—Cross section modified from Dott and Attig, 2004
33 Wildcat Mountain State Park
Mississippi River
MINNESOTA
IOWA
35 Vernon County Pillars
34 Pier County Park at Rockbridge
Silurian dolomite
Maquoketa Formation
Galena Dolomite, Decorah Formation and Platteville Formation
St. Peter Sandstone
Prairie du Chien Group
Shakopee Formation
Oneota Dolomite
Jordan Sandstone
St. Lawrence Formation
Tunnel City Group
Mazomanie Formation
Lone Rock Sandstone
Wonewoc Formation
Ironton Sandstone
Galesville Sandstone
Eau Claire Formation
Mt. Simon Sandstone
Precambrian
SIL
ORDOVICIAN
CAMBRIAN
40 Tower Hill State Park
41 Cave of the Mounds
Wisconsin River
Madison
39 Governor Dodge State Park
36 Wyalusing State Park
38 Mineral Point and Pendarvis Historic Site
37 Bevans Lead Mine
Dubuque, Iowa
ILLINOIS

THE DRIFTLESS AREA

The southwest corner of Wisconsin and adjoining smaller areas of Minnesota, Iowa, and Illinois were never touched by glaciers. Long ago the region earned the name Driftless Area because geologists did not find glacial till and other glacial material, collectively known as drift. While all the land around it was generally subdued by several glaciers and their collective deposits during the past 2.6 million years, the Driftless Area continued to be deeply eroded by water, wind, and the annual frost cycle, just as it had been for hundreds of millions of years before the Pleistocene ice ages.

The question of why the area was untouched by glaciers has been considered by geologists from around the world. The major lobes of the continental ice sheet were channeled to the south by lowlands now occupied by Lake Michigan and Green Bay and to the southwest by the Lake Superior basin. The ice of each of the several Pleistocene glaciations carved these lowlands deeper, channelizing each successive glacial advance. Highlands to the north of the Driftless may also have played a role in blocking the lateral movement of ice from the Superior Lobe.

If we could turn back the clock to a time before the Driftless Area began eroding, we would see a rocky plateau across most of Wisconsin. It would gently slope away from the central dome, dipping east toward the Michigan Basin and west and southwest toward other shallow basins. On the dome, erosion went to work on the upper layers, removing them and leaving the dome roughly ringed by escarpments where the upslope edges of more resistant layers of rock were exposed. With the creation of these escarpments, the sloping areas of the state became a series of cuestas—wide ridges with a gently sloping side and a steep side. One of these cuestas became known as the Prairie du Chien cuesta, named for the type of dolomite that once formed the bedrock of the rocky plateau and that is now eroding. Its escarpment today forms the ragged northeastern boundary of the Driftless Area.

Toward the end of the Wisconsin glaciation, a large glacial lake formed on the northeastern side of the Driftless Area. Ice blocked the flow of the Wisconsin River in south-central Wisconsin, and meltwater then backed up to form a roughly triangular-shaped lake that would grow to nearly the size of the present-day Great Salt Lake. Known as Glacial Lake Wisconsin, it existed for at least 3,000 years. Its waves and currents eroded the sandstone ridges of the flooded area, sifting sand to the lake bottom and filling the valleys. The area is now called the Central Sand Plain. Were it not for the deep glacial lake sediments, it would be part of the Driftless Area, which is why this chapter includes sites located on the plain.

30 PERROT STATE PARK

Mounds Stranded by an Ice Age River

Northwest of La Crosse on the Mississippi River, Perrot State Park encloses a small group of sandstone mounds and ridges separated from the rest of the Driftless Area by a wide plain arcing around their north and east sides. Geologists sorted out the story of how they became stranded by using clues from the Ice Age. Glaciers never covered Perrot State Park, which lies within the Driftless Area, but meltwater of the receding glaciers flowed by in a broad, braided stream that was an earlier version of the Mississippi River. Called Glacial River Warren, the ancient river coursed through the crescent-shaped plain to the north and east of the park. Southwest of the park, where the Mississippi is now, small northeast-flowing tributaries from the Minnesota side of the Driftless Area passed around both ends of the park on their way to the ancient river. The peaks and ridges of Perrot State Park were once on the Minnesota side of the Mississippi River.

Glacial River Warren, as well as the Trempealeau River, which now enters the Mississippi at the northwest end of the park, carried large loads of sediments from the retreating glaciers and gradually built a sandbar across Glacial River Warren where the Trempealeau joined it. About 50,000 years ago, the growing natural dam of sand blocked enough of the flow of the meltwater river to make it easier for the river to flow southeast through a channel that had been cut by one of its tributaries. The Mississippi's present course on the southwest side of the park area was soon established. The old riverbed north of the park became the wet plain it is today.

As the meltwater subsided, the broad, braided Mississippi River narrowed and cut a deeper main channel, leaving dry terraces on either side of it. Today the park's southeast entrance and the nearby town of Trempealeau sit on such a terrace about 60 feet above the river. Until about 10,000 years ago, the main channel might have been as much as 500 feet lower than it is today, making the bluffs nearly 1,000 feet higher than the ancient river. Over time, the river has filled much of this channel with sediment.

Whenever the meltwater slowed and areas of the floodplain were exposed to the sun, much of the deep silt brought by the meltwater dried and was picked up by winds. Clouds of this

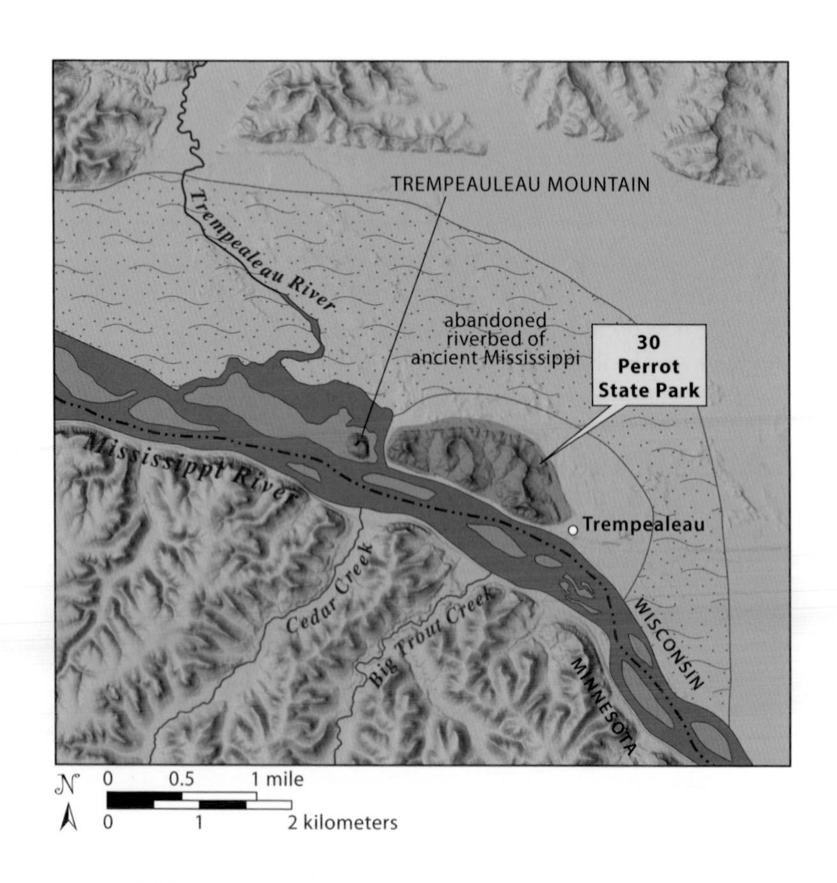

View to the west from Brady's Bluff showing Trempealeau Mountain (center) and river bluffs in Minnesota on the far side of the Mississippi River. The Trempealeau River flows from right to left across the center of the photo, cutting through the wide plain out of sight to the right (north).

An exposure of Galesville Sandstone on the trail to Brady's Bluff.

material, called *loess*, were blown across the land to the east of the riverbed, where they accumulated in layers as deep as 60 feet. This dark-colored soil enriches farm fields, and it underlies the park's hiking trails.

The park's most popular trails ascend Brady's Bluff, which looms high over the river, as is typical of the Mississippi River's famous bluffs. As you hike up the west side, you cross hundreds of thousands of years of sedimentary deposition for every foot of the climb. At its base is Cambrian sandstone of the Wonewoc Formation, deposited more than 500 million years ago. A member of the Wonewoc, the Galesville Sandstone, a brightly colored, whitish stone with marine fossils, is well exposed on the bluff. Overlying the Wonewoc are two more Cambrian sandstone formations, the Lone Rock of the Tunnel City Group and the Jordan Sandstone. A thin dolomite layer of the St. Lawrence Formation is sandwiched between them, deposited when the sea advanced and the Brady's Bluff area was farther from the sandy shore. All three Cambrian sandstone units are buff colored or yellowish to white, quite pure, with a high percentage of quartz. Their grains are well rounded, having been deposited and eroded several times by the Cambrian seas. These three sandstone formations each represent roughly a quarter of the bluff's height.

The top of the bluff is buff-colored Oneota Dolomite of the Prairie du Chien Group. Deposited early in the Ordovician Period, it is the first major sequence of carbonate rocks in Wisconsin. This resistant, massive rock was deposited in shallow waters far enough offshore to be relatively free of sand and silt. The distinctive Oneota Dolomite protects the softer, more erodible layers of sandstone beneath it.

31 GRANDAD BLUFF

Nearly Leveled for Building Stone

One of the highest and most striking river bluffs along the Mississippi is Grandad Bluff, towering 500 to 700 feet over La Crosse. The city lies on a stream terrace built of glacial sediments hauled here by the Mississippi River and its earlier versions. The bedrock under the sediments is Cambrian sandstone of the Eau Claire Formation, deposited about 530 million years ago by a slowly advancing sea. This fine-grained, thinly bedded unit contains shale with trilobite and brachiopod fossils but is not well exposed here, lying under the base of the river bluffs.

Grandad and its neighboring bluffs are composed of Cambrian sandstone overlain by Early Ordovician dolomite. From the base up are the Wonewoc and Tunnel City sandstones, a thin dolomite layer of the St. Lawrence Formation, and the Jordon Sandstone. The bluffs are capped by 50 feet of the Oneota Dolomite. Fast-moving meltwater draining Glacial Lake Agassiz (which occupied much of central Canada) filled the entire river valley at the end of the last glaciation. These waters swept tons of the sandstone away from the lower layers, undercutting the more resistant dolomite and creating the steep bluffs we see today.

Quarrying operations started on the La Crosse area bluffs in the late 1860s, prompted partly by a La Crosse city ordinance requiring that all new buildings be constructed of stone after several fires devastated the downtown area. From the north and south sides of Grandad Bluff, dolomite was blasted away and sent cascading down to the bluff's base, where it was collected and hauled away.

At the end of the nineteenth century, quarrying companies were preparing to expand these operations when local citizens led by Ellen P. Hixon, with the help of her husband and sons, launched an effort to protect the bluffs. The Hixons acquired the land and transferred it to the city of La Crosse, which established Grandad Bluff Park at the summit in 1912. Quarrying had halted completely by the 1930s. Since then, forest vegetation has reclaimed the scarred land, and some of the eroding sandstone has undergone case hardening—a process in which its surface becomes cemented by evaporating mineral solutions, making it more resistant to erosion. In addition to spectacular views over La Crosse, Grandad Bluff Park provides excellent information on the geological, natural, and human history of the area.

Grandad Bluff.

32 CASTELLATED MOUNDS OF THE CENTRAL SAND PLAIN

Ancient Islands in Glacial Lake Wisconsin

The Central Sand Plain occupies the former bed of Glacial Lake Wisconsin. On its southwest side, the Prairie du Chien Escarpment, capped by resistant dolomite, is gradually withering. Outlying fragments of it, along with an eroding bench capped with Ironton Sandstone to its east, stand on the plain as buttes, crags, and spires, often referred to as castellated mounds. When Glacial Lake Wisconsin occupied the Central Sand Plain, many of the mounds we see today, and many more that are now gone, stood for centuries as islands in that lake.

The Ironton bench is made of Galesville Sandstone overlain by Ironton Sandstone, both members of the Wonewoc Formation. The Ironton is relatively coarse-grained and well cemented by iron oxide and silica. The Galesville Sandstone is a loosely cemented stone that stands out on many landscapes because it is brightly colored to whitish. It is easily eroded and serves as the source of most of the sand in the Central Sand Plain. It is eroding out from under the more resistant Ironton Sandstone.

Geologists think the sandstone that forms the resistant tops of some mounds was cemented by calcium carbonate seeping from below the surface for millions of years while the sandstones were forming. Later, when the sandstone mantle over the state was being eroded by wind, rain, and streams, the softer sandstone surrounding these bodies of resistant sandstone eroded from around and under them.

When Glacial Lake Wisconsin occupied the sand plain, its eastern extent was contained by the Green Bay Lobe of the ice sheet. When it began to melt and retreat, the glacier calved icebergs into the lake. The glacial erratics found on the sand plain today were dropped there by ice rafts crossing the lake and releasing their loads of sand, gravel, and boulders as they melted. In some cases, icebergs rammed the islands and deposited debris there, which is why boulders and gravel can be found high up on some of the mounds.

Erosion continues today, with wind, rain, frost, and the roots of plants dismantling the bluff tops. While some of the sandstone has become case hardened—coated by a thin layer of harder sandstone cemented by evaporating mineral solutions —even that stone is vulnerable to erosion caused by hikers, climbers, and those wanting to leave their marks on the rocks. Only a few of the dozens of mounds in the Central Sand Plain are accessible from public land. Some of these have trails to their summits, where you can gain a view of other mounds scattered across the broad lakebed.

MILL BLUFF

Mill Bluff and a cluster of nearby bluffs encompassed within Mill Bluff State Park are located off US 12 near Camp Douglas. Standing 120 feet above the lakebed plain, Mill Bluff has a trail around its base and a set of steps to the top, which is capped by Ironton Sandstone. These bluffs are protected federally as a unit of the Ice Age National Scientific Reserve. The lower layers of sandstone in the mounds were deposited more than 500 million years ago by broad braided streams flowing across a sandy plain toward a sea coast.

CASTLE ROCK

Castle Rock, a few miles southeast of Mill Bluff off Interstate 90/94 near Camp Douglas, is accessible via a wayside. Hikers on the trail around the base of the rock get stunning views of the late Cambrian sandstones that are quickly eroding and thus maintaining their bright colors. The sandstone features prominent cross-bedding, evidence of the sandbars that formed as braided streams shifted continuously across the Cambrian lowland.

View from the top of Mill Bluff.

Castle Rock.

Weathering of the sandstone of Castle Rock.

Roche-Á-Cri.

ROCHE-Á-CRI

Rising 300 feet above the surrounding lakebed, Roche-Á-Cri, 16 miles east of Necedah, was a large island standing somewhere near the center of Glacial Lake Wisconsin. Its name, French for "rock that cries," was probably given by an early explorer referring to the shrieks of hawks and other raptors flying around its craggy peak. Its protective cap of harder Cambrian sandstone has mostly eroded away, so it is more subject to erosion than other mounds. Visitors to Roche-Á-Cri State Park can climb to the top of the mound on sturdy staircases, and the top is protected from human erosion by boardwalks and a platform that affords views of the ancient lakebed and several distant mounds. At the base of the mound, you can see Native American rock art created between 400 and 1,100 years ago.

The red layers in the cross-bedded sandstone in Roche-Á-Cri contain iron oxide.

SHIP ROCK

Ship Rock, about 10 miles east of Roche-A-Cri on WI 21, is a 100-foot-high, knife-edge pinnacle of Cambrian sandstone. It lies near the east side of the Central Sand Plain surrounded by a deep layer of outwash from the Green Bay Lobe, which stopped just a few miles east of Ship Rock. Were it not for this outwash, the pinnacle would be standing about 200 feet above the plain. A vertical crack visible on the west end of Ship Rock runs along its axis. Geologist John Luczaj suggests that the crack could have conducted a silica-rich solution that cemented the quartz sandstone on either side of it, making the stone harder and more resistant to erosion. Visitors can get close-up views of the pinnacle and observe signs of the erosion by braided streams and glacial lake waves that shaped this and other such structures on the sand plain.

Streams and waves eroded the cross-bedded sandstone of Ship Rock, pictured here at its west end.

The west end of Ship Rock.

33 WILDCAT MOUNTAIN STATE PARK

Coulee Country of the Driftless Area

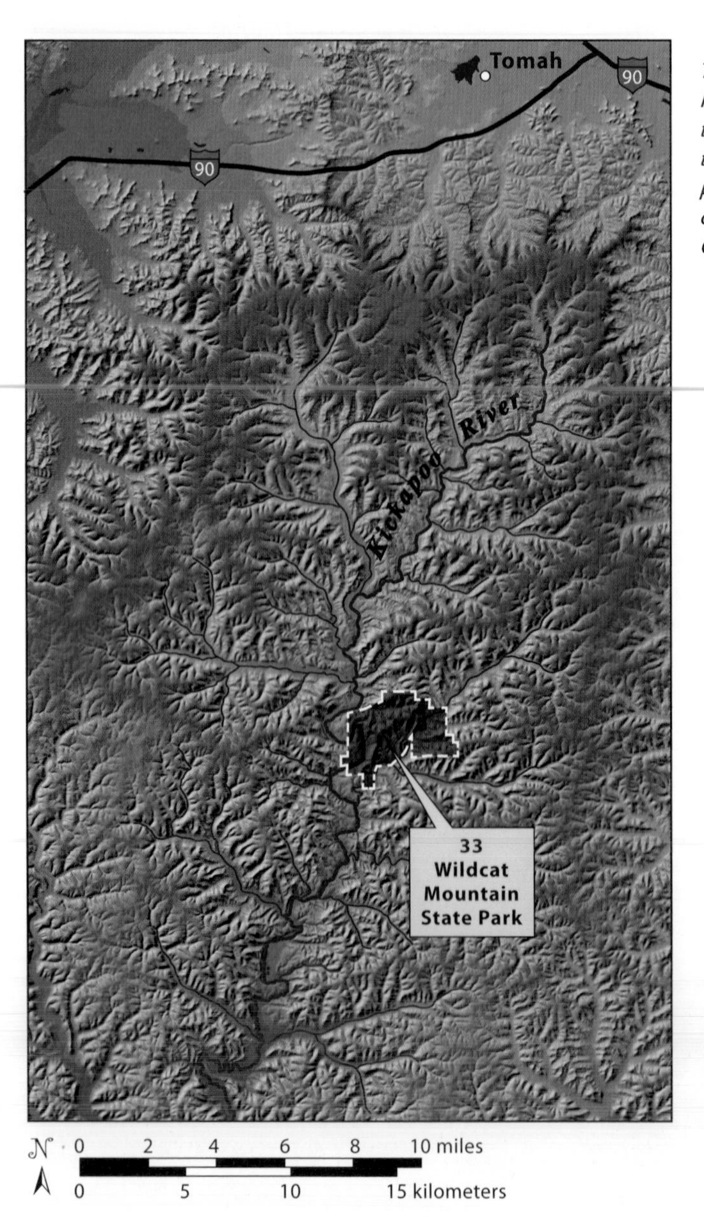

The Kickapoo River features the dendritic, or treelike, drainage pattern that characterizes Coulee Country.

You can drive among the ridges, hills, and hollows of the Driftless Area and get a good sense of the sharply varying terrain that was never touched by glaciers. For hikers and canoeists, however, perhaps the best close-up exposure to this landscape is found in Wildcat Mountain State Park. Trails ascend from the floor of the Kickapoo River valley to the tops of the ridges—as high as 390 feet above the valley floor—taking hikers through time, from the late Cambrian to the Early Ordovician Period. Canoeists on the Kickapoo River float among ancient rock outcroppings that rise dramatically above the river.

Kickapoo is Algonquin for "he moves about, standing now here, now there." The Kickapoo River meanders so much that it travels 125 miles through a drainage basin that is half as long. Feeding this river are dozens of small tributaries with steep valleys. The resulting landscape pattern is called *dendritic*, which means "branching like a tree." The deep stream valleys that form the tree branches are called "coulees," from the French word *couler*, which means "to flow." The Kickapoo River valley is classic coulee country.

The river flows in sandstone of the Wonewoc Formation, deposited around 500 million years ago. Above this formation, a thick sandstone layer of the Tunnel City Group is characterized by dark glauconite crystals that probably formed around the fecal remains of ancient marine animals that lived in a shallow sea. This major layer is topped by a thin layer of harder dolomite of the St. Lawrence Formation, grading up into the buff-colored to reddish Jordan Sandstone, the youngest of the Cambrian strata. The mounds in the park are capped by Early Ordovician dolomite of the Prairie du Chien Group, laid down about 480 million years ago in a shallow sea after it had advanced over all of Wisconsin. Wind, flowing water, and the annual frost cycle have carved elaborate shapes in the softer sandstone within the mounds of the park. Some of the hiking trails give visitors close-up views of these erosional sculptures.

A state natural area within Wildcat Mountain State Park protects rare stands of old-growth white pine and hemlock. Hidden deep in Coulee Country, this location is one of only a few places in Wisconsin that avoided the axes that leveled the vast forest in the late 1800s and early 1900s. These species grow well in the cool, moist climate found on the park's sandstone mounds.

Sandstone outcrop eroded by water and centuries of weathering.

View of the Kickapoo River valley from Wildcat Mountain.

PIER COUNTY PARK AT ROCKBRIDGE

Eroded Joint in a Sandstone Ridge

Lying along the west side of the Pine River in Richland County is a bold north-trending ridge of sandstone, about a half mile long, standing 60 feet above the surrounding plain. The south end of this sandstone mass lies within Pier County Park on WI 80 next to the village of Rockbridge. The north end lies on private land. The ridge is fragmented into several blocks by joints, or deep vertical cracks, and has been deeply eroded at its base on both its east and west sides by streams that have flowed on one or both sides at various times throughout its history. Today, the West Branch of the Pine River flows southeast toward the ridge where it has worked its way through one of the joints and under the sandstone mass to join the Pine River on the east side of the ridge. During flooding, both streams lap against the ridge, continuing their erosive work.

Where the West Branch cuts through the ridge, it has eroded stone along the joint to make a triangular passage, known as the Rockbridge, about 20 feet wide and 10 feet high. At the ridge's south end, at some point in the distant past, an overhanging slab of stone broke off and now stands upright like the point of a giant sword driven into the land. Long ago a road ran through the gap between the sandstone mass and this broken piece. That road is now a dead-end parking area that allows for easy viewing of the natural bridge.

The site has not been studied extensively, so there remains some uncertainty among geologists about the composition of the sandstone. The top layers of the ridge could be composed at least partly of sandstone of the Tunnel City Group, deposited around 500 million years ago in Cambrian time. The Ironton Sandstone, a strongly cemented member of the Wonewoc Formation, which underlies the Tunnel City, might be another component. Its iron oxide and silica cement resists erosion, so

The West Branch of the Pine River flows beneath Rockbridge—an eroded passage along a joint between blocks of sandstone. This is the east side of the bridge.

the Ironton Sandstone is responsible for many of the resistant ridges in the Driftless Area. The reddish streaks in the sandstone at Pier County Park indicate the presence of iron. The more erodible sandstone near the water level could be that of the softer member of the Wonewoc, the Galesville Sandstone. Cross-bedding, or sweeping layers in the sandstone, indicate that wind-formed sand dunes once lay here, probably near a Cambrian seashore.

Archeologists have found evidence in Pier County Park that Native Americans used the overhangs of the sandstone for shelter during winter months. The land was donated to Richland County in the early 1920s in order to preserve its unique beauty. Workers excavated a tunnel that allows visitors to walk through to the other side of the ridge. Stairways on both sides of the ridge take visitors to it summit where a path runs the length of it within the park.

Cross-bedded sandstone at the Rockbridge, one of the lesser-known jewels of the Driftless Area.

A view of the west side of the sandstone ridge looking north. The West Branch of the Pine River flows to the base of the sandstone mass then north along its base to Rockbridge (out of sight at center).

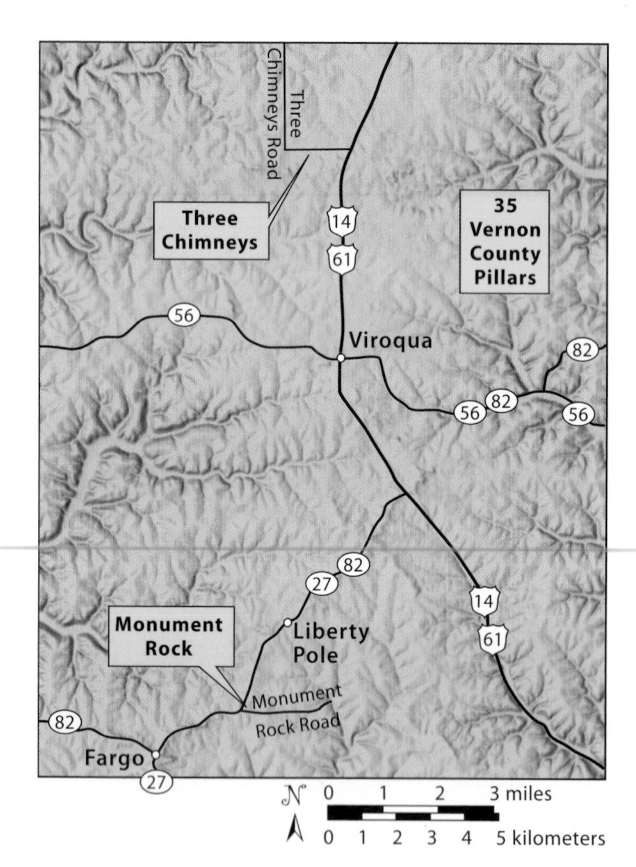

35 VERNON COUNTY PILLARS

Sculptures in Case-Hardened St. Peter Sandstone

Vernon County lies in the heart of the Driftless Area, every square mile of it occupied by ridges and valleys that were never glaciated. Viroqua, the county seat, sits on a wide, flat-topped ridge running north to south across the middle of the county. The ridge is at least 20 miles long and 5 to 6 miles wide, and both sides of it descend quickly through networks of stream valleys and deep hollows—classic Driftless country.

Most of the ridges in the county are capped by dolomite of the Prairie du Chien Group, deposited by an Early Ordovician sea beginning about 485 million years ago. When this sea retreated, the dolomite was exposed to millions of years of erosion until another sea advanced and deposited St. Peter Sandstone on a highly uneven layer of eroded dolomite. The renowned Wisconsin geologist Fredrik T. Thwaites described what might have been the scene near Viroqua: "The waters of the St. Peter sea advanced through many narrow channels between islands and ridges of dolomite."

Monument Rock, a pillar of St. Peter Sandstone.

Look for the face of a troll etched by natural erosion into the top left of the rightmost pillar at Three Chimneys.

The dark surface of Monument Rock is case-hardened sandstone.

Several Paleozoic Era seas deposited more layers of sandstone, dolomite, and shale, but all of those layers, including most of the St. Peter Sandstone, were eroded away in the Driftless Area during several hundred million years. However, on the top of much of Vernon County's central high ridge, a layer of St. Peter Sandstone remains. In this sandstone, a variety of pillars were whittled and carved by the long period of erosion. Fragile looking but ancient and enduring, the pillars have survived partly because of the process of case hardening, in which sandstone is cemented on its surface by the evaporation of mineral-bearing solutions.

There are at least five sets of pillars in Vernon County. All are at least viewable, standing 40 to 80 feet above the surrounding land, but not all are on public land. Monument Rock stands on a patch of public land next to WI 27/WI 82 south of Viroqua. Visitors should not try to park on the busy, hilly highway but instead can park on the side of a county road that leaves the highway just south of the rock. Monument Rock is 40 feet high and twice as wide at the top as it is at its base.

Another group of pillars is Three Chimneys, a few miles north of Viroqua on Three Chimney Road, west of US 14. These three columns of rock appear to have sprouted from the rolling plain, taking peculiar shapes as they grew. In reality, they are all that is left of the once-thick layer of sandstone. They sit on private land, but you can view them from across the farm field next to the road.

The trail to Treasure Cave, overlooking the confluence of the Wisconsin and Mississippi Rivers, passes through a crevice in the dolomite near the top of the bluff. This feature is known as the Keyhole.

36 WYALUSING STATE PARK

Confluence of the Wisconsin and Mississippi Rivers

The southwest corner of the state, where the Wisconsin River joins the Mississippi River, has long attracted people because of its important travel routes. When the French and English began vying for control of the area in the late 1700s, the river bluffs overlooking the valleys became strategically important because they commanded a view of the entire confluence. The bluffs on the south side of the confluence became one of Wisconsin's first state parks—Wyalusing State Park, established in 1917.

The bluff tops, which stand 500 feet above the confluence, are made of Oneota Dolomite of Early Ordovician age, part of the Prairie du Chien Group. The group is named for other exposures near the city of Prairie du Chien, Wisconsin's second-oldest city, located on the north side of the confluence. The Oneota grades from sandy at its lower reaches to more pure dolomite at its highest levels, indicating the area was covered by a slowly deepening sea in Early Ordovician time. As the shoreline advanced northward, the sediments deposited in the sea contained less sand from streams pouring into it and more calcareous remains of sea creatures that lived in deeper water.

Under the dolomite layers, the bluffs are composed of Cambrian sandstone. The park's trails lead to three shallow sand caves, eroded by water and wind, in which hikers can see orangish and reddish sandstone layers colored by iron oxides. These large overhangs provided shelter for Native American groups in the distant past. Chemical erosion has also been at work in the higher dolomite layers in the park area, creating karst features, including small sinkholes, cavities and crevices, and springs. The park's popular Treasure Cave is a karst feature.

A broad stream terrace extends for several miles east on the north side of the Wisconsin River, and another one extends north on the east side of the Mississippi River. The town of Prairie du Chien, along with well-traveled WI 35 and WI 60 and a busy railroad, lies on these terraces beneath the river bluffs. The uppermost terrace next to the bluffs is composed of glacial outwash up to 200 feet thick, carried by meltwater flowing in the ancient Mississippi from the ice lobes to the north and in the Wisconsin River from ice retreating east. Post-glacial flooding filled the valleys from bank to bank, eroding the softer sandstone and undercutting the overlying dolomite, contributing to the relief of the imposing river bluffs.

Multicolored sandstone at Big Sand Cave in Wyalusing State Park.

Cavities in this dolomite in the Wyalusing bluffs show centuries of chemical erosion.

37 BEVANS LEAD MINE

Ore Deposit in Galena Dolomite

The lead and zinc deposits in southwestern Wisconsin are thought to have formed around 245 million years ago at the beginning of Triassic time. An upheaval of land 600 miles to the south (now in Tennessee and Arkansas) forced groundwater to flow northward within deep rock layers. The water was heated to temperatures high enough to dissolve minerals in the rock, which it carried into what is now northern Illinois and southwestern Wisconsin. Under pressure, it flowed toward the surface and into the openings that had been chemically eroded along joints and bedding planes in the dolomite bedrock. There it cooled and the minerals precipitated, forming deposits of lead, zinc, and smaller amounts of other minerals.

These deposits lay mostly within the Galena Dolomite with smaller deposits found in the Decorah and Platteville Formations—all Middle Ordovician–age dolomite with some shale interspersed. They are exposed mostly south of the Wisconsin River, in the far southwestern Driftless Area. Stark displays of these dolomite bedrock layers can be seen in expansive roadcuts along several highways in southwestern Wisconsin. The thickest layer, at a fairly even 225 feet, is the Galena Dolomite. Galena, a lead sulfide, is Wisconsin's official state mineral.

Near-surface lead deposits in a roughly kite-shaped area that straddles the corners of southwestern Wisconsin, northwestern Illinois, and northeastern Iowa were gathered and used for centuries by Native Americans. Deposits partially exposed by erosion were easy to find because galena forms distinctive cube-shaped crystals, and fresh exposures have a shiny luster. European immigrant miners got wind of the deposits and began arriving in the area in the 1820s, bringing on a lead mining boom in what was to become known as the lead district. Shortly after the Civil War, the lead boom ended, but a zinc boom soon began, lasting from the late 1860s through the 1970s.

Several towns grew up and flourished around the richer lead and zinc deposits. One such town was Platteville, located in the southwestern quadrant of Wisconsin's lead-mining area and the namesake of the Platteville Formation. At one time, at least thirty-one mining companies were incorporated within the city. Mining ended in the 1970s, but one Platteville lead mine has been preserved as a historical attraction. The Bevans Lead Mine and museum are located near the center of the city.

In 1845, attorney Lorenzo Bevans decided to try mining and discovered a particularly rich vein of lead in the Galena Formation at what was then the western edge of Platteville. Bevans and

Galena lead ore. —Specimen on display at the UW Geology Museum

Mannequins are posed as miners in the Bevans Lead Mine.

his workers removed more than 2 million pounds of ore before the year was out. The underground mine was open for only a few years, but it produced at least 1,000 tons of lead per year during that period. At some unknown time it was sealed off but was reopened in the 1970s and opened to the public in 1976.

The museum displays a collection of photos, artifacts, maps, old mining equipment, dioramas, and placards with historical information on all aspects of mining. A guided tour takes visitors through part of the old mine, as well as through a two-story headframe and hoist house where machines lifted ore out of the mine in large buckets. Workers separated the mineral from the waste rock using sledge hammers and other hand tools. Tour guides provide detailed information that gives visitors a sense for just how grueling the mining life could be.

MINERAL POINT AND THE PENDARVIS HISTORIC SITE

Lead and Zinc Mining in the 1800s

Mineral Point Hill, an angular highland situated between two converging stream valleys, once contained rich deposits of lead and zinc along with smaller deposits of copper and iron. Native Americans gathered the near-surface lead for centuries. White miners learned of the lead deposit in 1827 and, as immigrant miners moved in, the ensuing mining boom created Mineral Point, the third-oldest city in Wisconsin.

Lead mining was highly lucrative in its early days. The near-surface lead deposits could be easily collected from shallow pits, and fortune-seeking miners dug thousands of holes all over the lead district. The miners were called "badgers," possibly because their pits were larger versions of the holes dug by those tough, persistent burrowing mammals. Another possible source of this nickname is the fact that many early lead miners made shelters of, and lived in, their pits by covering them with tree branches, sod, or scrap building materials. These mining badgers were the inspiration for the state symbol and the mascot for the University of Wisconsin–Madison's sports teams.

When the near-surface lead deposits were depleted, miners began to dig tunnels and shafts to reach underground deposits, typically not deeper than 50 feet. In the 1830s, miners from Cornwall, England, having exhausted that country's tin and copper deposits, heard of the lead boom in the Upper Mississippi Valley and began migrating there. The Cornish brought with them valuable know-how gained from their experience with deep-shaft mining. Miners were lowered into a shaft in a large bucket connected to a windlass. Such buckets were then used to haul out the mined ore. Miners roasted the ore in open-pit

The top of a mining shaft with bucket and windlass on Mineral Point Hill.

hearths near the mine sites, collected the resulting molten lead, and cooled it in flat saucer-shaped casts, which were then hauled to mills for further processing.

In the 1840s Wisconsin's lead producers supplied more than half the nation's lead. The population of the state's lead district, most of it located in Mineral Point, swelled from two hundred to more than ten thousand in a few years. By 1845, lead mining had peaked, and fifteen years later zinc mining took off and the economy once again boomed. The city's zinc-ore processing plant, built in 1886, was for a time the largest in the world. Zinc mining peaked in the late 1930s and ended in the 1970s.

Among the Cornish immigrants were skilled stonemasons who built dozens of small but sturdy houses of dolomite and sandstone quarried from the hills. Several

Pendarvis house, built in the mid-1800s by Cornish immigrants and named for the Pendarves estate in Cornwall, has been the site of a restaurant and lodging.

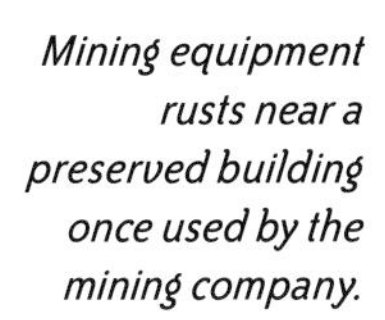

Mining equipment rusts near a preserved building once used by the mining company.

Downtown Mineral Point, with its historic architecture, attracts tourists who come to sample the area's history. —Courtesy SV Heart Photography

of these Cornish houses are still standing in Mineral Point and other towns of the lead district. The best-known houses are preserved in the Pendarvis Historic Site, operated by the Wisconsin Historical Society. The site is along the northwest side of Mineral Point Hill on Shake Rag Street. Several popular stories recount how the street got its name, best known of which is that the wives of the miners would shake rags to signal the workers up on the hill that lunch was ready. A more likely explanation is that "shake-rag" was a nineteenth-century term sometimes given to a wretched or rough, untamed person or place, and the early mining camps would have certainly fit that description. Across Shake Rag Street on the hill, you can take a self-guided tour of the Merry Christmas mine site and view two closed-off shafts that took miners down to nine interconnected tunnels. You can also see old buckets and windlasses used to haul ore and miners out of the shafts, a reconstructed open-pit roasting hearth, and the fading depressions of several collapsed badger holes.

While the economy thrived, the region's environment suffered considerably. The area was stripped of its trees, which were used to fuel the open-pit smelters and heat the homes. Many of the barren hillsides were pocked with mining pits and marred by waste rock piles. Without their vegetation, the hills were severely eroded, with runoff carrying toxic sediments into nearby streams. Smoke from the smelters polluted the air. The Wisconsin Department of Natural Resources has cleaned up most of the area's lead and zinc tailings piles. On the mine hill, what was once an environmental eyesore is now a flourishing prairie, one of the largest restored prairies in southwestern Wisconsin. With these historic and ecological preservation efforts, Mineral Point has turned from mining the rocks to mining its own rich history.

39 GOVERNOR DODGE STATE PARK

Variable Hardness in the St. Peter Sandstone

Enee Point stands tall because the St. Peter Sandstone is case hardened.

Governor Dodge State Park, 3 miles north of Dodgeville on WI 23, showcases Ordovician-age rock exposures, primarily the St. Peter Sandstone. The fascinating rock formations resulted from the varying rates of erosion among the different rock layers. The lowermost rock, underlying the park, is dolomite of the Prairie du Chien Group, deposited by an early Ordovician sea beginning about 485 million years ago. The next layer up, the St. Peter Sandstone, can be very soft but is often made more resistant through case hardening, in which a cement or crust is formed on its surface by the evaporation of mineral-bearing solutions. One of the first features that visitors see when entering the park is Enee Point, a case-hardened cliff of St. Peter Sandstone, which, although quite resistant, can still be damaged by visitors who want to carve or climb on the rocks.

The St. Peter Sandstone was deposited about 470 million years ago by broad braided streams carrying sand to the shore of an advancing sea. Wisconsin was in the tropics, and warm winds formed high sand dunes that were eventually drowned by the sea. Cross-bedding in the lower half of the St. Peter Sandstone in the park reflects this wind deposition, and the upper half shows signs of a shallow marine environment, including *Skolithos*, vertical fossil tubes that ancient worms burrowed into the sandy bottoms near the shore.

The uppermost layer of stone, which forms the bedrock in the higher areas of the park, is the Platteville Formation. It was laid down around 460 million years ago as the Ordovician sea deepened, depositing progressively less sand and more remains of sea creatures, and eventually became limestone that was then converted to dolomite.

The St. Peter Sandstone is starkly displayed at the Deer Cove Rockshelter, less than 1 mile east of Enee Point. Visitors taking the trail from the Deer Cove parking area can get a close-up view of cross-bedded dune sandstone. The trail takes hikers to the left end of the wall, up a steep slope to a point nearly level with the overhang of harder sandstone that overlies the dune sand. The thin, vertical ribs on these layers are *Skolithos* trace fossils.

At Stephens Falls, another prominent feature of this park, a small stream drops over harder layers of St. Peter Sandstone to the softer dune-formed layers below. Over thousands of years, the stream wore away at the hard layer so that the falls migrated upstream, creating the wide, horseshoe-shaped end of the canyon.

As long as 8,000 years ago, Native Americans occupied the rock shelters in the park during winter months. Several springs flowing from the porous sandstone layers provided fresh water throughout the year. Later, immigrant farmers built springhouses to pool the fresh water and use it for drinking and preserving perishable foods. A number of farm families worked the uplands during the middle and late 1800s.

In 1948, Iowa County donated one of the farmsteads to the State of Wisconsin to create the park. Eventually the state purchased more farmland to create and expand the park. Dams were built across the two branches of Mill Creek to form the two lakes that now lie in the park. Lakes are rare in the well-drained sandstone of the Driftless Area, so these lakes attract many regional residents to this geological showcase park.

At the Deer Cove Rockshelter, resistant layers near the top of the cliff provided protection for early Native Americans. They also protected the softer dune-formed sandstone below.

Skolithos, *fossil burrows, in the St. Peter Sandstone.* —Specimen in the collection of the University of Wisconsin Geology Museum

Along the Pine Cliff Trail, a stream created an arch in a hard layer of sandstone by eroding the softer rock below.

Stephens Falls drops 30 feet over a resistant ledge of St. Peter Sandstone. Note the alcove at lower left where water has eroded the softer sandstone.

40 TOWER HILL STATE PARK
Manufacture of Lead Shot

Some of the lead mined in Wisconsin was used to make lead gunshot during the mid-1800s. The story of how that shot was manufactured is well preserved at Tower Hill State Park, named for the shot tower built on top of a high bluff overlooking the Wisconsin River. One way to make lead shot is to have drops of molten lead fall a certain distance through the air to form spheres before landing in water to cool. Green Bay businessman Daniel Whitney wanted to make use of the bluff and river for manufacturing and shipping lead shot, and he hired Thomas B. Shaunce, a young lead miner, to help him do so. Only the top 60 feet of the bluff is vertical, so a 120-foot shaft had to be chiseled through the lower section to permit a straight drop of 180 feet. A 90-foot tunnel connected the bottom of the shaft to the riverside face of the bluff. Against the vertical cliff face, a 60-foot wooden structure, or tower, was built to direct the falling lead into the lower shaft.

It took Shaunce and a partner 187 days in 1831 and 1832 to complete the job. They used only hand tools—pickaxes, gads, a plumb bob, buckets, and a windlass—and made limited use of gunpowder to loosen the harder rock at the base of the bluff. Shaunce dug the tunnel at the base, working inward from the face of the bluff at the river's edge. When he broke through the last of the rock connecting the tunnel to the shaft, pressure from the column of air in the shaft blasted him to the rocky ground. The injuries he received, including a collapsed lung and probably a concussion, plagued him for the rest of his life.

The view from inside the tunnel.

The shot company operated for nearly thirty years, closing down in 1861 due to an economic downturn and reduced demand for its product. The town of Helena, located on what is now the picnic area of the park, housed and served the workers but quickly faded away after the company went out of business.

At Tower Hill State Park, located on County Highway C, which connects WI 23 to US 14, a series of trails takes visitors to the historic bluff and down to the river where a short section of the tunnel from the shaft is still open for exploration. The trail to the tunnel runs along the old oxcart trail used to haul deformed lead shot back up to the bluff top. From the main trail out of the parking area, a spur trail to the base of the reconstructed wooden tower takes hikers to a close-up view of the sandstone layers in the top 60 feet of the bluff—the buff-colored Tunnel City Group overlying the lighter-colored, harder Wonewoc Formation near the base. Cross-bedding in some of the strata indicates that sand dunes periodically existed here before they were submerged by advancing Cambrian seas.

The sandstone bluff and the reconstructed shot tower.

The riverside oxcart trail, now a hiking trail.

41 CAVE OF THE MOUNDS

Colorful Speleothems in Galena Dolomite

Erosion has scoured away most of the Silurian dolomite that once lay over all of Wisconsin. Its remnants exist in the Niagara Escarpment on the eastern side of the state and on the tops of several mounds in the southwest corner, which are outliers of the more widespread Silurian strata now eroding to the south in Illinois and Iowa. Two of these mounds, called the Blue Mounds, are located about 20 miles west of Madison on US 151. The western mound is the higher of the two, standing 415 feet above the surrounding plain, the highest point in southern Wisconsin and the site of Blue Mound State Park. The eastern mound is 230 feet shorter.

Colors in the flowstone of Painted Waterfall are reflected in the pool.
—Courtesy Cave of the Mounds

Cave of the Mounds, a few miles east of the state park on the south face of the eastern mound, was discovered in 1939 when a routine dynamite blast at a quarry uncovered a 20-foot-high room with passages to other chambers. The landowner immediately halted the quarrying and, within a year, opened a commercial cave. Lying in Galena Dolomite deposited about 460 million years ago, the cave is 70 feet deep and about a half mile long. Groundwater, made weakly acidic by carbon dioxide absorbed from the environment, dissolved calcium carbonate along fissures and bedding planes in the dolomite, creating crevices and caverns. Percolating water combined with the sulfur in lead and other minerals deep underground to form sulfuric acid, which also dissolves calcium carbonate.

Iron-rich formations, called Bleeding Stalactites, in Cave of the Mounds.
—Courtesy Cave of the Mounds

At Cave of the Mounds, this dissolution process began between 1 and 2 million years ago when the dolomite was below the water table. As the local streams carved their valleys deeper, the water table dropped and underground erosion continued at deeper levels. Eventually, groundwater rivulets and then streams flowed through the cave, enlarging the passageways, and water dripped into the spacious caverns. Upon interacting with the air, the water's carbon dioxide escaped, triggering the deposition of calcium carbonate (the mineral calcite). Cave of the Mounds is famous for its spectacular dripstone formations, collectively called *speleothems*, that grew slowly as the calcite was deposited, crystal by crystal. One cubic inch of growth can take one hundred years or more. It is important to never touch any of the formations to avoid accidentally damaging them. Also, oil from our skin can interfere with the deposition of calcite and stop the growth of the speleothems.

Cave of the Mounds, designated a National Natural Landmark in 1988, is open for touring throughout the year. Many caves close during winter to allow resident bats to hibernate undisturbed. However, this cave was a closed underground system until it was discovered and quickly sealed in 1939, and there is no evidence that bats have ever lived in it. Thus, the cave remains open in winter when its temperature is an even 50 degrees, just as in summer.

The Gem Room in Cave of the Mounds displays three aspects of speleothem formation: prominent stalactites and stalagmites (center), flowstone (lower center to lower left), and color—red showing the presence of iron oxides in the calcite and blues and grays showing the presence of manganese oxides.
—Courtesy Cave of the Mounds

South Cavern shows a variety of speleothems, including flowstone, where water, flowing in sheets, deposits layer upon layer of calcite on the walls or inclined floor of a cave.
—Courtesy Cave of the Mounds

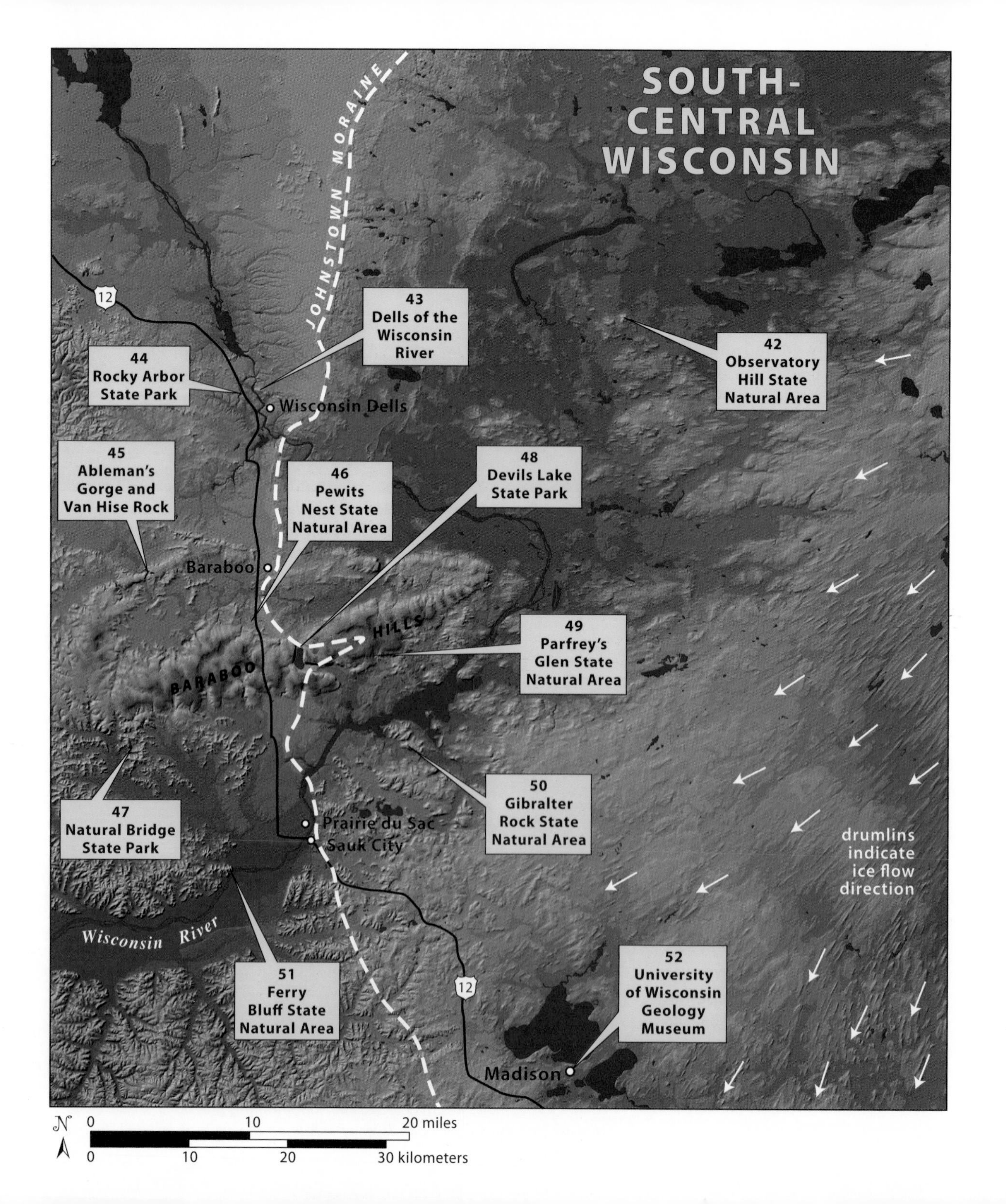
SOUTH-CENTRAL WISCONSIN
JOHNSTOWN MORAINE
43
Dells of the Wisconsin River
42
Observatory Hill State Natural Area
44
Rocky Arbor State Park
Wisconsin Dells
45
Ableman's Gorge and Van Hise Rock
46
Pewits Nest State Natural Area
48
Devils Lake State Park
Baraboo
BARABOO HILLS
49
Parfrey's Glen State Natural Area
50
Gibralter Rock State Natural Area
47
Natural Bridge State Park
Prairie du Sac
Sauk City
drumlins indicate ice flow direction
Wisconsin River
51
Ferry Bluff State Natural Area
52
University of Wisconsin Geology Museum
Madison
12
0 10 20 miles
0 10 20 30 kilometers
N

SOUTH-CENTRAL WISCONSIN

Glaciers, glacial lakes, and fast-flowing meltwater shaped many of the surface features of south-central Wisconsin. Areas that were leveled by the moving masses of ice lie adjacent to areas never touched by any glacier. Geologists from all over the world have traveled to this region to study the juxtaposition of glaciated and unglaciated land. The underlying bedrock, however, successfully competes for the geologists' attention.

Around 1,760 million years ago, granitic magma intruded the late Archean and early Proterozoic bedrock under the surface, feeding violent volcanic explosions that rocked a wide area of southern Wisconsin. The erupted lava cooled into rhyolite, a dense, fine-grained reddish volcanic rock, the extrusive equivalent of granite. About 50 million years later, this volcanic activity had ended and a sea invaded the Wisconsin area of the continent—the first of many shallow seas that advanced and retreated during the next 1.5 billion years.

The earliest of these seas was fed by broad, braided rivers flowing out of the eroding Penokean Mountains to the north. They deposited a thick layer of quartz-rich sand over much of Wisconsin. The sand was eventually converted to sandstone and much later buried under other sedimentary layers. By 1,650 million years ago, much of this sandstone had been folded, metamorphosed to quartzite, and heaved up, possibly as a result of a continental collision to the south. Large bodies of the pinkish to purple rock, called the Baraboo Quartzite, are exposed today in the Baraboo Hills.

During the mountain building process, flat land was compressed and crumpled or wrinkled, just as wrinkles form in a rug when its ends are pushed together. In the Baraboo Hills, the layers of quartzite were pushed up into roughly parallel east-west folds with a low downfold forming between them, called the Baraboo Syncline. Quartzite layers in the north fold were heaved up to a near-vertical tilt. The south fold was less severe, the layers being tilted just 20 to 30 degrees from horizontal.

A billion years of erosion gradually leveled the mountains, leaving behind ridges of resistant, folded quartzite. Starting

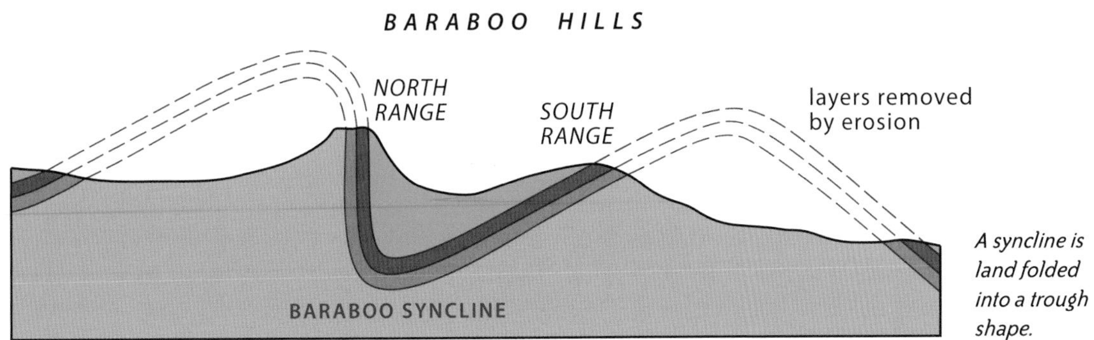

A syncline is land folded into a trough shape.

around 500 million years ago, several Cambrian and younger Paleozoic seas invaded the area and over time deposited layers of sedimentary rock. Some of the higher quartzite hills in southern Wisconsin stood as islands in the seas. After the seas finally departed for good, at least 200 million years ago, erosion carried away much of the softer Paleozoic rock layers, leaving several peaks and ridges of Precambrian and Cambrian rock standing above eroded plains. The north and south ranges of the modern Baraboo Hills are primarily composed of resistant rock on the limbs of the Baraboo Syncline. The ranges are not in fact parallel but converge somewhat like the gunnels of a rowboat with its prow pointing east. Its stern on the west end of the ranges is a jumbled arrangement of hills running roughly north and south. For our purposes, we focus on the north and south ranges—the gunnels of the boat.

Striations on this rhyolite at Observatory Hill show the passage of the Green Bay ice sheet.

42 OBSERVATORY HILL STATE NATURAL AREA

A Former Mountain of Precambrian Rhyolite

Observatory Hill in southern Marquette County stands 300 feet above the surrounding countryside. At the summit is an outcropping of 1,760-million-year-old rhyolite, with tiny feldspar crystals embedded in the dense, fine-grained volcanic rock. The rhyolite is a Precambrian inlier, a resistant mass of older rock surrounded by younger, less-resistant rock. The old rock body was an elevated area in Precambrian time that was gradually surrounded and probably buried by sedimentary rock in Paleozoic time. One of the best descriptions of the contrasting types of rock comes from Gwen M. Schultz, Wisconsin geographer and author of *Wisconsin's Foundations*, who described Observatory Hill and other such inliers as "once-molten, contorted, intruded, crystalline, or otherwise igneous or metamorphic in character . . . a distinct contrast to the younger, nearly horizontal sedimentary strata framing them."

Since 1989, the summit of Observatory Hill has been a state natural area that protects a rock glade plant community dominated by red cedar and hosting the state-threatened slender bush clover (*Lespedeza virginica*). To climb the hill on a trail, go south from Montello on County Highway F about 3 miles to 14th Road, which you follow south just over 2 miles to 13th Road, then south another 1.5 miles to the site. At the summit, you can find polished rhyolite with striations, or scratches in the rock, left by the grinding ice of the Green Bay Lobe and earlier glaciers that pulverized and removed much of the surrounding softer sandstone.

Observatory Hill has long been the destination of naturalists, including John Muir, who tramped through this part of Wisconsin years before he began exploring the High Sierra of California. A few miles southwest of the hill is John Muir Memorial County Park, located near the site where Muir's father homesteaded after emigrating with his son from Scotland.

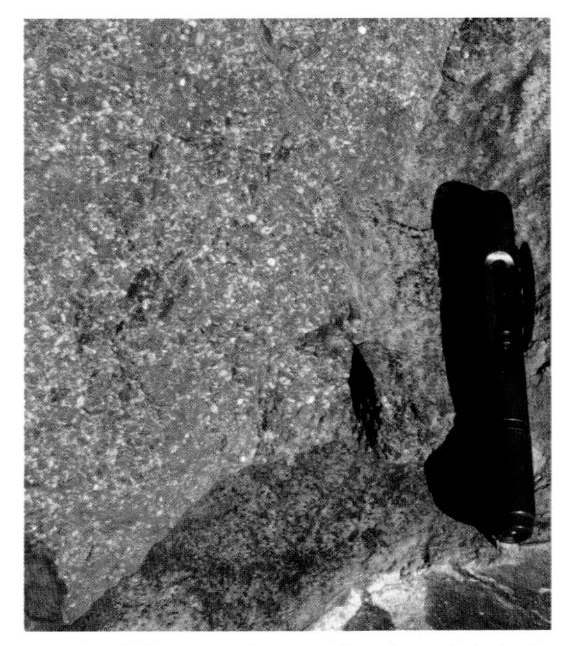

Tiny white feldspar crystals are visible in the pinkish rhyolite.

The summit of Observatory Hill.

Cross-bedded sandstone.

43 DELLS OF THE WISCONSIN RIVER

Carved by a Catastrophic Flood from Glacial Lake Wisconsin

One of Wisconsin's oldest tourist attractions is a spectacular sandstone gorge through which the Wisconsin River flows, fed by streams flowing in smaller but equally striking canyons. Called the Dells of the Wisconsin River, this network of beautiful canyons is somewhat overshadowed by the city of Wisconsin Dells, a gaudy and famous collection of water parks, amusement venues, and other attractions. However, the Dells north and south of the city have been largely preserved in their natural state.

The gorge lies in late Cambrian sandstone, deposited around 500 million years ago. While some geologists once thought it to be Mt. Simon Sandstone, the consensus is that it belongs to the Wonewoc Formation. The gorge walls display layers of the Wonewoc's Galesville Sandstone, a weakly cemented stone that erodes easily so that its fresh exposures are light colored and striking. It is capped by a thin layer of Ironton Sandstone, which is much more strongly cemented by iron oxides and silica. The differential erosion of these two members of the Wonewoc Formation results in the overhangs, cliffs, and other extraordinary features that make the Dells famous. The sand was deposited by braided streams flowing broadly over the region to the retreating shore of a Cambrian sea. Winds molded the increasingly exposed sand into dunes, forming the cross-bedding in the Galesville Sandstone.

During the Wisconsin glaciation, the Green Bay Lobe stopped advancing a few miles to the east of the Dells. The ice impounded Glacial Lake Wisconsin, which submerged the Dells area and spread out to the north and west. The Johnstown Moraine, deposited beneath the ice margin, contributed to the tenuous dam. As the glacier melted, this fragile dam was diminished and at some point it gave way, draining the vast glacial lake within a few weeks. Its water funneled through the Dells area, quickly stripping away glacial lake sediments, cutting through the Ironton Sandstone, and carving the gorge and its smaller tributary canyons out of the much more erodible Galesville Sandstone.

The 7-mile-long gorge, averaging 150 to 200 feet wide, was possibly hundreds of feet deep after the flood, but since then the river has filled much of the gorge with sand and other sediments. Modern cliffs stand as high as 100 feet over the water. The best way to see the cliffs is from a boat, and during summer the gorge sees heavy traffic of power boats. A trip downriver affords views of the deep, narrow tributary canyons, such as Coldwater Canyon, Artists Glen, and Witch's Gulch. The latter has been outfitted with a boat dock at its mouth and a boardwalk from the river to the head of the canyon, where developers have built a concession stand with restrooms. Visitors can see how the rushing meltwater eroded the rock along prominent vertical joints and spun gravel and small boulders within eddies to carve potholes. These features tell geologists that the canyon was created by fast-flowing meltwater, as opposed to slow stream erosion or faulting. Witch's Gulch is

Prominent joints, or deep vertical cracks, separate blocks of sandstone in the Dells. The darker stone on top, the Ironton Sandstone, overlies the lighter Galesville Sandstone.

100 feet wide at its mouth and narrows to as little as 2 feet on the way to the concession building.

Another famous and popular erosional feature accessible by boat tour is Stand Rock—a 46-foot-high column of Galesville Sandstone capped by a disk-shaped slab of Ironton Sandstone. The column is 6 to 8 feet in diameter, and the tabular cap is 20 feet in diameter and 4 to 6 feet thick. The renowned photographer H. H. Bennett, who made a career capturing the Dells' iconic rocks on film in the late 1800s, famously photographed his son leaping the gap between the main mass and the top of Stand Rock. The hike from the river to Stand Rock and back affords views of several other spectacular erosional features.

In 1909, a dam built in the City of Wisconsin Dells raised the level of the river by 16 feet. Prime examples of cross-bedded sandstone, photographed by Bennett and others before the dam was built, are now underwater. Thin strips of land along both sides of the river in the Upper Dells (the stretch north of the town) have been designated a state natural area, and thus they are protected from development. Little in the way of human structures is visible from the river, and a few trails provide limited access to the riverside and to views of rock cliffs.

Witch's Gulch, a narrow tributary canyon with 30-to-40-foot-high walls.

Stand Rock was once part of the sandstone mass standing a few feet to the south of it but was separated by centuries of erosion by water, wind, and frost action.

44 ROCKY ARBOR STATE PARK

Abandoned Channel of Wisconsin River

The same cataclysmic event that shaped the Dells of the Wisconsin River—the rapid drainage of Glacial Lake Wisconsin—also carved a small gorge 1 mile west of the Dells, now the site of Rocky Arbor State Park. On the park's trails, hikers can get close-up views of unique sandstone features carved by flowing water. The Wisconsin River once flowed through this canyon, but sometime in the past 10,000 years, long after the ice age and flood, it abandoned the Rocky Arbor gorge and found another section of the flood-eroded dells, 1.5 miles to the east, where it flows today.

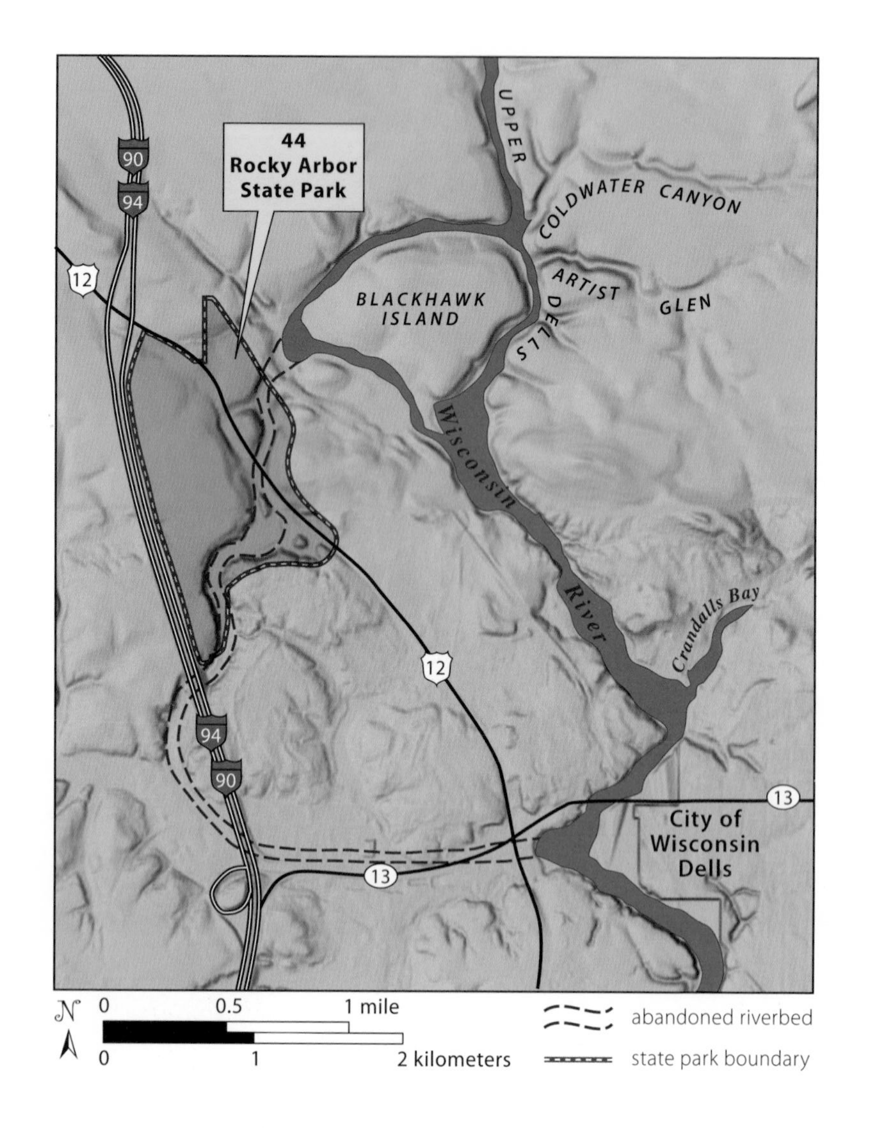

The course change occurred through a process called stream capture, which started with a small tributary flowing to the east of Rocky Arbor. The headwaters of that tributary eroded the sandstone bedrock, working their way west to the gorge in present-day Rocky Arbor State Park. When this erosion broke into the valley, the river found the tributary streambed to be the path of least resistance and abandoned its Rocky Arbor channel. Now only a small stream flows within the former riverbed.

The abandoned canyon—about 1.25 miles long, less than 0.5 mile wide, and 60 to 90 feet deep—hosts a wetland at its base. The exposed sandstone is buff colored to brown and belongs to the same formation as the Cambrian sandstone in the nearby gorge of the Dells—the Wonewoc. In addition to water-carved sandstone, hikers also see large tilted blocks of sandstone that fell from the upper reaches of the canyon walls. Such features are reminders of the fact that erosion by water, wind, frost, and the prying roots of vegetation continues in Rocky Arbor today.

A former island in the ancient Wisconsin River now stands alone in Rocky Arbor.

A sandstone block has fallen down and now leans against the wall of the Rocky Arbor gorge.

45 ABLEMAN'S GORGE AND VAN HISE ROCK

Deciphering the Baraboo Syncline

Ableman's Gorge, where the Baraboo River cut through the west end of the north range of the Baraboo Hills, provided geologists numerous clues for figuring out the mystery of the Baraboo Syncline. To reach the gorge, head a few miles north of Rock Springs on WI 136. The 200-foot-deep gorge, also called the Upper Narrows, is a half-mile long, with cliffs and an old quarry exposing the rocks. The most obvious features in the gorge are vertical beds of massive quartzite. Cross-beds and ripple marks in the quartzite, which was originally sand deposited on the shore of a sea sometime around 1,700 million years ago, tell geologists that the top of the vertical bedding layers, the "up" direction, is to the south.

A 15-foot pillar of rock reveals a great deal more about how these rocks became vertical. This distinctive monolith, designated Van Hise Rock Natural Historical Landmark, is named for Charles Van Hise, a renowned geologist and former president of the University of Wisconsin–Madison. Around 1900, he used this pillar to help explain how the orientation of cleavage in folded rock can tell you the shape of the fold and an outcrop's position in the fold. The UW Geology Department website notes that "Van Hise, using the Baraboo Hills as a classroom, made Wisconsin internationally famous as a center of geological research and education."

The pillar is a relatively tiny remnant of three layers of rock that were folded and tilted from horizontal to vertical during the formation of the Baraboo Syncline. A dark layer of slate is sandwiched between two layers of massive pink quartzite. The long vertical crack separating the two different types of rock is the bedding layer. The many parallel lines in the dark slate, slanting at an angle to the bedding, is cleavage, a planar pattern that develops in some folded metamorphic rock. The slate contains flat minerals that aligned during metamorphism to create the cleavage. The massive, uniform quartzite does not contain cleavage because it is made of the mineral quartz, which is not a planar crystal. The relationship between cleavage and bedding tells us that Van Hise Rock is on the north limb

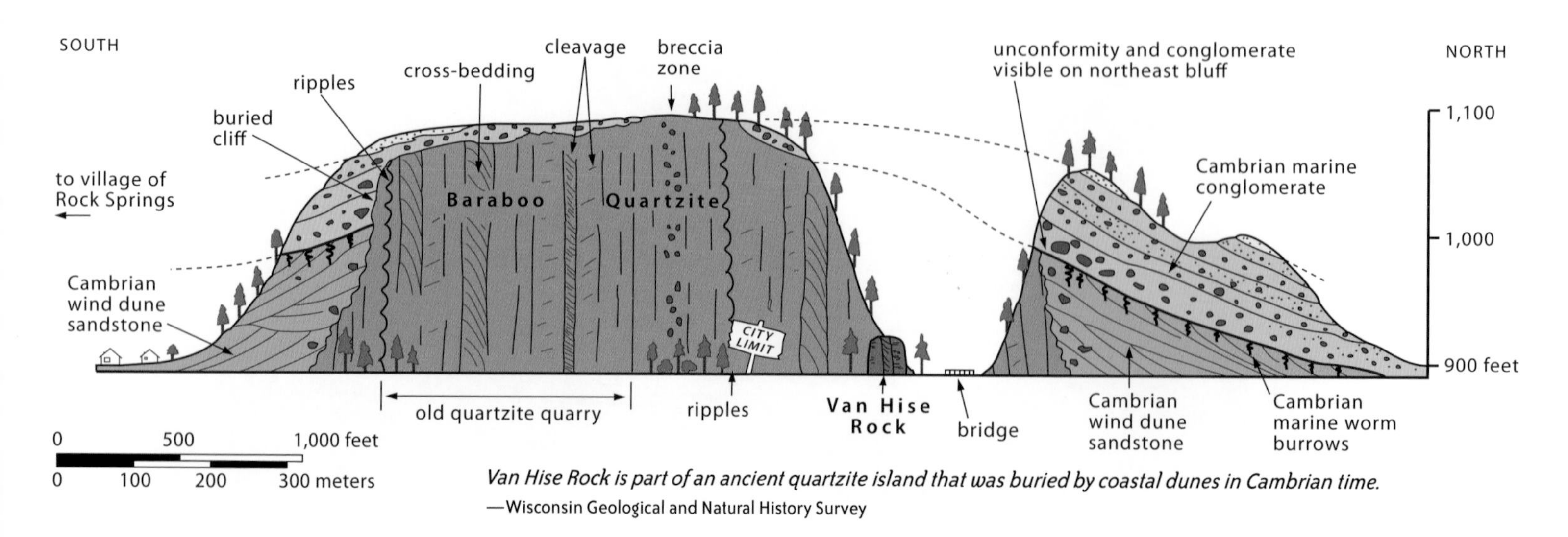

Van Hise Rock is part of an ancient quartzite island that was buried by coastal dunes in Cambrian time.
—Wisconsin Geological and Natural History Survey

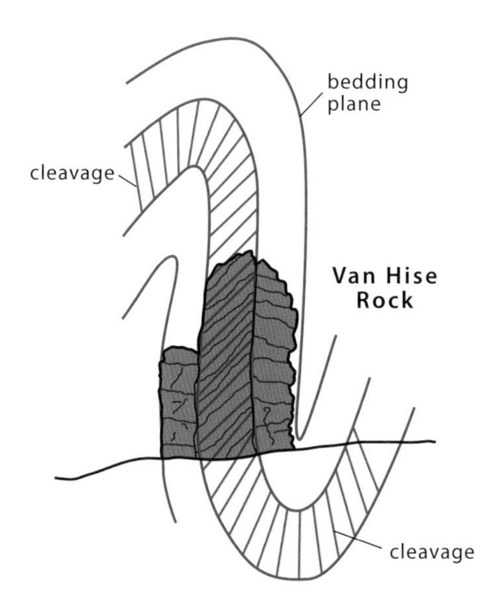

The cleavage (green) and bedding planes (blue) in Van Hise Rock.

The bedding plane at Van Hise Rock is the vertical dark crack, with cleavage in the slate on the left side and massive quartzite on the right side.

Van Hise Rock is one of the most famous and instructive rock features in the world.

of the downward fold, or syncline. The folding occurred during a mountain building event 1,650 million years ago that compressed these rocks from the south.

More clues in Ableman's Gorge tell us what happened to these folded rocks 500 million years ago in Cambrian time. Overlying the top ends of the vertical quartzite layers in the quarry wall is a thin layer of Cambrian conglomerate—boulders of quartzite within sandstone. Similar conglomerate is covering the sloping cliff of quartzite on the south end of the quarry. On the north end of the gorge, the cliff across the river also shows visible layers of the flat-lying Cambrian strata overlying the vertical layers of quartzite. Under the conglomerate

The wall of the abandoned quarry shows the vertical layers of Precambrian rock covered with horizontal layers of Cambrian conglomerate.

on both ends of the gorge is thickly cross-bedded sandstone of Cambrian age.

Geologists have determined that in Cambrian time, these vertical beds of quartzite were part of an island with coastal dunes. Wisconsin was still south of the equator, so storm waves of the tropical sea regularly pounded the island. Chunks of quartzite, loosened by erosion and waves, plunged into the sea and were tumbled and rounded for centuries and eventually covered by sand. Piles of rocks and sand at the base of the cliffs eventually became the horizontal sandstone and conglomerate that now surround and cover the ancient island. Geologists Robert Dott and John Attig paint a more detailed picture of this story in *Roadside Geology of Wisconsin*.

Ripple marks from an ancient sandy seashore can be found on the south wall of the abandoned quarry. The distance from top to bottom in this photo is 14 feet.

Looking north through Ableman's Gorge: the west wall is on the left, the east wall is out of the photo, and the north wall, where the gorge curves to the west, is ahead. Van Hise Rock is to the right.

46 PEWITS NEST STATE NATURAL AREA

A Hermit's Hideaway in Wonewoc Sandstone

Pewits Nest State Natural Area is a small, scenic gorge in the valley of Skillet Creek, which drains a part of the south range of the Baraboo Hills (see map on page 125). This 40-to-60-foot-deep canyon, located 2 miles southwest of Baraboo on County Highway W, was carved by fast-flowing icy water draining from Glacial Lake Baraboo, a southern extension of Glacial Lake Wisconsin, after the ice dam impounding that lake was breached. Probably within a few weeks, these waters swept away the deep glacial lake sediments and cut down through sandstone to create this 300-yard-long gorge. During and since the meltwater flood, the stream has created waterfalls and large potholes in which pools have formed.

Unlike other gorges described in this chapter, this one drops north into the interior lowland of the Baraboo Syncline, so it cuts through rocks deposited in the Cambrian sea that existed between the two ranges of Baraboo quartzite islands. The gorge walls are thinly bedded, fine-grained reddish sandstone of the Wonewoc Formation. Sandstone beds of the same age deposited outside the syncline are relatively thick-bedded and coarse-grained with beds of conglomerate interspersed. Protected by quartzite islands, the seawater within the syncline was likely quieter and less roiled by waves than the open sea outside the syncline, where storm waves regularly crashed against the sea cliffs. In the quiet water, smaller grains settled to the bottom, forming the fine-grained sandstone.

While the name Pewits Nest now refers to the entire gorge, it originally was given to a hideaway inhabited by a settler in the 1840s. Local historian H. E. Cole wrote about the "eccentric tinker," who remains unnamed in historical reports. The man made his living repairing everything from watches to farm equipment, and he carved a workshop shelter into the sandstone wall of the gorge 10 feet over one of its pools. This ingenious mechanic created the space in such a way that it was visible from only one angle deep in the little canyon and accessible only through trapdoors. To one observer, the shelter resembled the nest of a phoebe, a bird that used to

The fine-grained Cambrian sandstone in Pewits Nest.

Moss-covered rocks surround a pool at the bottom of Pewits Nest.

be called a "pewit" or "pewee," and the man's workshop was subsequently called Pewits Nest.

The repairman was also a fiddler, storyteller, and Mormon preacher who dabbled with medicine in his later life. He built a water wheel in the gorge to turn his lathes and to run a coffee mill. After he abandoned the site, some other unnamed party operated a sawmill there, installing a 34-foot water wheel with a 9-foot shaft in the narrow gap between the sandstone walls at the mouth of the gorge. Nowadays, one might not guess that this secluded place was once the site of so much industrial activity. No signs of the mill or the hermit's shelter remain in the gorge.

Instead of industry, recreation is now the main influence on the gorge—so much so that the Wisconsin Department of Natural Resources closed the narrow, deep part of the gorge in June 2017. The site had become popular as a swimming hole and a place for rock climbing and cliff jumping. The activities damaged the cliff ecosystem and also resulted in a rising number of injuries. Swimming, climbing, and cliff jumping can now draw heavy fines. In 2017, plans were approved for the building of stairways, designated trails, and railings to allow safe viewing of a small part of the gorge and to protect its natural beauty. These improvements are due to be completed by 2019.

47 NATURAL BRIDGE STATE PARK

Deconstructing a Sandstone Arch

In the shadow of the south range of the Baraboo Hills, 17 miles northwest of Sauk City, is Natural Bridge State Park, home of Wisconsin's largest sandstone arch. The natural bridge is made of an unusually hard, well-cemented type of Cambrian sandstone from the Mazomanie Formation of the Tunnel City Group. The arch is 25 feet high and 35 feet long with an interior height reported to be between 15 and 18 feet.

Two theories have been proposed for the arch's origin. Some geologists think the arch was formed by many centuries of erosion caused by water seeping through the sandstone, freezing in winter, and expanding to weaken the rock. Although the Green Bay Lobe of the ice sheet stopped 12 miles east of the arch, the harsh conditions of the Pleistocene Epoch would have enhanced such frost action. With little vegetation at the edge of the ice sheets, winds could have scoured away weak zones in the sandstone, creating and enlarging the arch.

Other researchers have hypothesized that the arch may be a remnant of a cave roof or part of an ancient sinkhole. The calcium carbonate content of the sandstone is relatively high, so the arch could be a solution feature—one formed by chemical erosion by slightly acidic water. The orientation of the arch and the regional groundwater flow direction conform to karst landform orientations in southwest Wisconsin, further supporting the hypothesis. However, comparison of this arch with those in other areas of the country suggests that it most likely was formed by mechanical erosion by water, frost, and wind.

Within the arch are layers of conglomerate containing quartzite stones that likely came from a quartzite sea stack at the edge of the Cambrian sea. The stones were carried about a half mile by storm-driven ocean currents to where they were buried by sand and later converted to conglomerate. Sediments deposited by later seas buried the Cambrian layers, but erosive forces have since broken down and carried away all but the most resistant masses of sandstone in the area, one of which forms the natural bridge.

Under the arch is a prominent overhang of hard sandstone used for centuries as a rock shelter by different groups of Native Americans. Like the arch, it was formed by the erosion of weaker sandstone underlying more strongly cemented layers. Archeologists first excavated this shelter in 1957 and concluded it was used possibly as early as 12,000 years ago. They discovered the bones of about fifty species of animals that must have been used for food or other purposes.

Many of the names and initials carved in the stone near the overhang probably date from the time when European immigrants first came to the area. In the 1890s, some locals decided it would be a good place for a dance floor and bar, and they dug away a layer of sand and rocks to level the area under the rock shelter, destroying much of the ancient historical record. By the 1920s, large numbers of tourists were visiting the arch and rock shelter, and some concerned area residents were calling for action to protect the site. The land remained private until the 1970s, when its owners sold it to the state, and in 1973 it became a state park.

Sandstone arches are inherently fragile and can collapse over time. Hundreds of people climbing and walking on it every day would destroy it within a few years or decades. For this reason, climbing on the arch is prohibited by state law.

The natural bridge and rock shelter in Cambrian sandstone.

48 DEVILS LAKE STATE PARK

Ancient Valley in Baraboo Quartzite

Devils Lake State Park attracts an average of 1.5 million visitors per year. Many flock to the lake to swim, sail, or paddle, but others come to see the park's spectacular geologic legacy. Not only is the park an Ice Age National Scientific Reserve, one of nine established in Wisconsin to preserve and study evidence of glaciation, it also showcases folded Precambrian Baraboo Quartzite and Cambrian sandstone.

The park's geologic story begins in Precambrian time, around 1,700 million years ago, when deep beds of sandstone, thought to be 4,000 feet deep in the area of the park, were metamorphosed to quartzite during a mountain building episode. The Baraboo Quartzite is an extremely hard rock colored reddish to purple by films of iron oxides. At some unknown point in Precambrian time, a stream valley developed in the mountains, crossing the south range of the Baraboo Hills where Devils Lake now lies.

Geologists estimate that when the Cambrian sea first encroached on the hills around 500 million years ago, they stood as islands up to 1,000 feet above the seafloor. Frequent storm waves slammed the islands, loosening and pulling chunks of quartzite down into the surf, where they were tumbled and rounded for centuries. After these shorelines were buried in sand during another cycle of deposition, the rounded boulders of quartzite embedded in sand became conglomerates, which today are exposed high up on some cliff walls.

In the Paleozoic Era, seas deposited layer upon layer of sandstone, shale, and limestone, and all or most of the islands were buried under the sedimentary rock. By 200 to 300 million years ago, the last sea had come and gone, and the sea bottom was subject to rapid erosion. In the late Mesozoic or early Cenozoic Era, perhaps between 150 and 50 million years ago, a fast-flowing river became established in the old Precambrian valley. It carried away layers of sandstone and other sedimentary rock and carved the gorge we see today. Gravel and rocks spinning in the eddies of the fast-flowing river drilled potholes into the quartzite. The potholes are located along the Devils Doorway and Potholes Trails, high up on a south-facing bluff where the river, flowing at least 400 feet above the current lake level, veered east in the gorge. The river and other erosional processes partly exhumed the old quartzite islands, which now stand as high as 500 feet above the surrounding land.

Beginning about 2.6 million years ago, several glaciers inched into Wisconsin. About 19,000 years ago, the Green Bay Lobe moved in from the east and flowed partway across the Baraboo Hills and into the north and south ends of the gorge, where it stopped, forming a 200-foot wall of ice at each end. The glacier acted as a conveyor belt, bringing sand, gravel, and boulders from its interior to the margin, where they were dropped for centuries to form the high morainal ridge—the Johnstown Moraine—that now spans the gorge on either end of the lake. The glacier was held back by highlands east of the East Bluff, so that the moraine connecting the two ridges follows a serpentine line within the park's borders.

Trails take hikers along the tops of both the East and West Bluffs, affording spectacular views of the park and its surroundings. The West Bluff Trail yields a view of the entire East Bluff and the glacial moraines that flank it on the north and south. Talus fields—the long slopes of fragmented quartzite piled along the bases of the bluffs—accumulated during the frigid conditions of the Pleistocene Epoch. Water entering the cracks and crevices of the quartzite cliffs during warmer months froze and expanded during winter and gradually pried loose chunks of quartzite that then fell from the cliffs, some of them shattering into smaller boulders. The freeze-thaw cycle is also responsible for some of the iconic rock formations still standing on the bluffs, such as Devils Doorway and Balanced Rock. We know the glacier never covered this part of the park because, although the rocks weigh many tons, they almost certainly would have been knocked over by a 200-foot wall of moving ice.

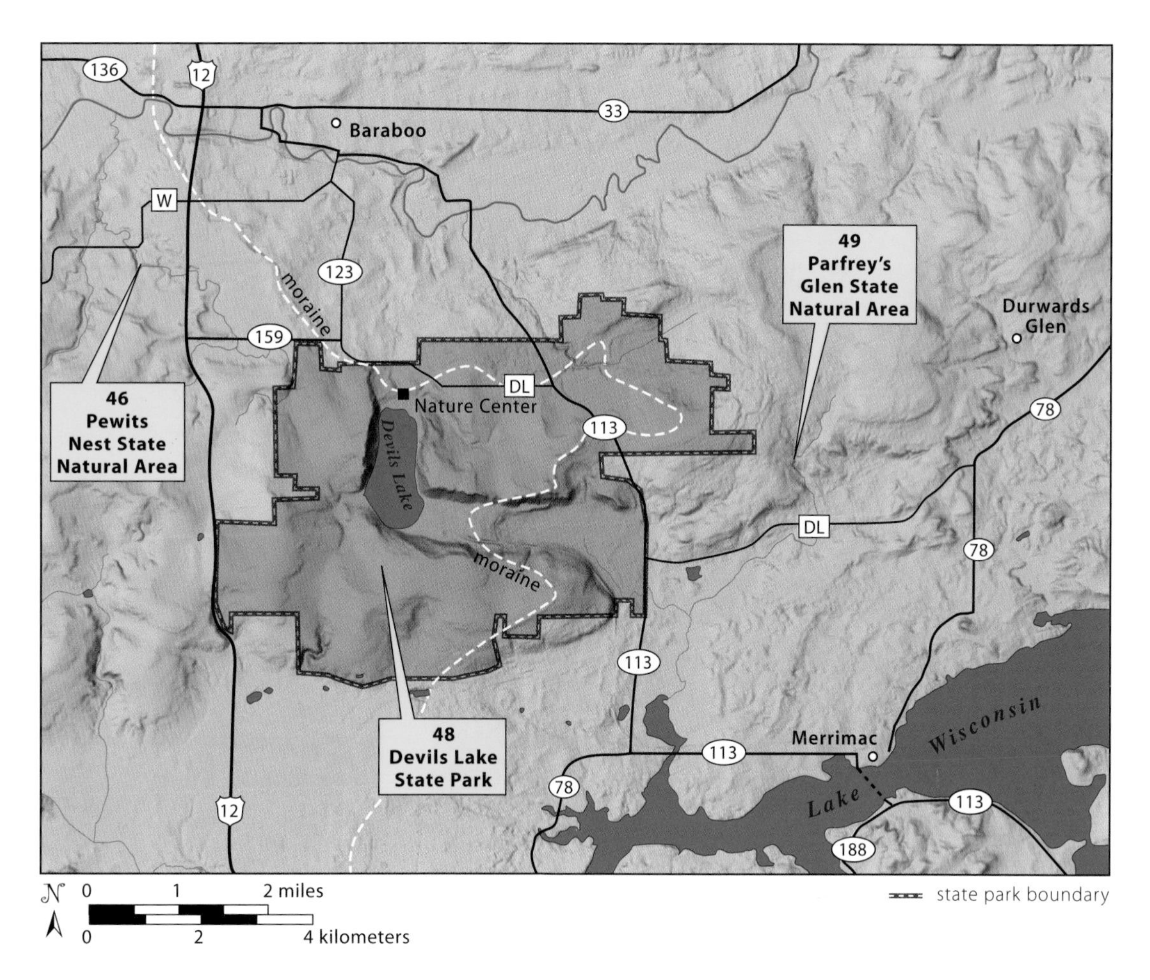

The vegetation pattern on East Bluff reflects the underlying rock layers, which slope down about 20 degrees to the left, or north, dipping into the Baraboo Syncline.

Quartzite and sandstone conglomerate in Devils Lake State Park.

The talus slopes at Devils Lake have quartzite boulders as big as 10 feet across.

Look for ripple marks on some of the flat quartzite surfaces used to make the trails and on quartzite boulders in talus slopes at the bases of the cliffs.

Devils Doorway, a product of the extreme freeze-thaw cycles during the ice ages, dramatically displays Baraboo Quartzite.

By around 16,000 years ago, when the climate was warming and the glacier was melting back, Devils Lake was considerably deeper than it is now. Huge volumes of meltwater flowed into the lake, depositing sediment. Geologists estimate that glacial lake sediments are 300 to 380 feet deep. Since those days, the lake has stabilized at a depth averaging 40 feet.

The Nature Center, high on the moraine at the north end of the lake, has an excellent collection of informative displays. The 150-foot-high moraine at the south end can be viewed from some trails and from Roznos Meadow, east of the lake. It forms the heavily forested backdrop for the south-shore beach, picnic, and camping areas. The park is well equipped with shelters, campgrounds, and trails, all built by Civilian Conservation Corps workers in the 1930s. Their mission was to make the park more visitor friendly and safe while preserving the remarkable natural features that make it so popular.

49 PARFREY'S GLEN STATE NATURAL AREA

Meltwater Gorge in Cambrian Conglomerate

The Green Bay Lobe of the continental ice sheet covered the eastern third of the Baraboo Hills. When the glacier receded around 10,000 years ago, torrents of meltwater carved several steep-sided gorges in the glaciated area of the hills. One of the best examples is Parfrey's Glen, located on the south side of the South Range, 4 miles east of Devils Lake on County Highway DL (see map on page 125). A spring-fed stream flows in the 100-foot-deep gorge and occasional flooding influences the vertical walls, but an ancient meltwater river did almost all the work of creating the gorge. The presence of partial potholes high up on the east wall in the narrowest part of the glen is evidence of this powerful stream. Whirling water spun boulders and gravel in eddies, creating pot-shaped and cylindrical holes in the rock, some of them quite large.

The glen lies in a massive body of Cambrian sandstone and conglomerate, a distinctive combination that earned the name Parfreys Glen Formation. When Cambrian seas invaded the area, islands of Baraboo Quartzite were battered frequently by storm waves. Quartzite blocks, loosened by the waves, dropped into the sea and formed cliffside rock piles. The quartzite blocks were broken, tumbled, and rounded for centuries by the waves and currents. Eventually sand and other sediments filled the spaces among the rocks and buried the rock piles and cliffs, resulting in widespread beds of conglomerate interspersed with beds of more pure sandstone. The quartzite pieces in the conglomerate vary in size from that of pebbles to boulders. The

Conglomerate layers are prominent in Parfrey's Glen.

Close-up view of quartzite conglomerate in Parfrey's Glen.

sea cliff that the quartzite was derived from lies buried a few hundred feet west of the innermost part of the gorge, or to the left for hikers entering the gorge.

In the late 1800s, a settler named Robert Parfrey operated a saw mill and grist mill in the glen. He dammed the creek in the inner gorge and built a large waterwheel there. After he was gone, increasing tourist traffic began damaging the glen's natural features. The state acquired the land and designated the glen as the first state natural area in 1952. With its moist, cool conditions, it supports vegetation normally found only in the northern part of the state, including yellow birch and mountain maple.

The Department of Natural Resources built a substantial set of boardwalks, stairs, and viewing platforms all the way into the end of the gorge where the creek cascades down from the hills. In 2008, a ferocious flood destroyed most of these structures, and earlier flooding had done similar damage. The state decided that the risk of such flooding in the gorge is too high to justify rebuilding the boardwalks. Visitors can still get to the end of the gorge after a 0.7-mile hike, but it involves crossing the stream and scrambling over large boulders, and caution is advised. Climbing on the gorge walls is prohibited. The upside of the flooding is that you can now see the gorge in its nearly natural state.

Geologists Robert H. Dott Jr. and John W. Attig provide a superb account of the Parfrey's Glen story in their book *Roadside Geology of Wisconsin*. It is the source of much of this description.

Part of a large pothole remains high in the upper east wall of the glen (right side as you head into the glen).

Gibraltar Rock viewed from the southwest.

50 GIBRALTAR ROCK STATE NATURAL AREA

Outlier of St. Peter Sandstone

As the Wisconsin River rounds its big bend at the east end of the Baraboo Hills, it slows and widens upon entering Lake Wisconsin, a flowage created by the dam downstream at Prairie du Sac. Just downstream of the widest part of the lake, the Merrimac Ferry runs cars and people back and forth across the river between Merrimac on the north bank and Okee on the south, as it has since 1844. Stretching southeast from the ferry landing on the south bank is a small range of hills, the highest of which is called Gibraltar Rock.

The hill is a little over 1 mile southwest of Okee off County Highway V. It stands about 400 feet above a large bog and broad area of farmland to the southwest. (Most sources say it rises only 300 feet, but the US Geological Survey puts its elevation at 1,247 feet above sea level, more than 400 feet above the flat plain.) At the top of the southwest side of the hill is a 100-foot-tall cliff, striking because its light-colored sandstone glows yellowish or even reddish, depending on light conditions. It is thought that early landowners named the rock after the famous Gibraltar Rock on Spain's southern Mediterranean coast.

Gibraltar Rock is an outlier of St. Peter Sandstone, deposited by an Ordovician sea and long since eroded away from most of Wisconsin. The closest large exposures of this stone are more than 20 miles to the south. At the base of the hill is Cambrian sandstone overlain by Prairie du Chien dolomite, which forms the body of the hill. The St. Peter Sandstone caps the hill and forms the vertical cliff. A veneer of glacial till covers the top of the hill, evidence that it was glaciated. It lay only a few miles from the western edge of the Green Bay Lobe, so was not buried as deeply under ice as was the area to the east. Thus the hill was not dramatically reduced by the glacier, which rounded off its east and northeast sides but left the cliff of St. Peter Sandstone as it appears today.

The site was designated a state natural area in 1969, partly to protect the hill's forest of red oak and basswood and its dry prairie bordered by a stand of red cedar, an increasingly rare ecosystem. It was operated as a county park until 2007 when Columbia County transferred it to the Wisconsin Department of Natural Resources. A parking area on County Highway V permits access to an old road, closed to motorized traffic, that runs steeply up the northeast side of the hill. Hikers might prefer the segment of the Ice Age National Scenic Trail that starts at the same point and winds through the woods on a gentler climb to the top of the cliff and then back down on the west side of the hill to another parking area on County Highway V. The trail comes close to the cliff edge overlooking sheer drops of at least 100 feet. The scenery is gorgeous, but caution is advised.

View of an agricultural plain to the southwest from the top of Gibraltar Rock.

FERRY BLUFF STATE NATURAL AREA

Meltwater Erosion on Outer Bend of Wisconsin River

Ferry Bluff State Natural Area encompasses two sandstone bluffs that loom 300 feet above the Wisconsin River. Known as Ferry Bluff and Cactus Bluff, both are dramatic examples of the scenic cliffs along rivers in the Upper Midwest, especially the Mississippi and its large tributaries.

Ferry Bluff as viewed from the Wisconsin River. —Courtesy Jeff Bach

At river level, the sandstone in the bluffs belongs to the Wonewoc Formation, which lies beneath the lighter-colored sandstone of the Tunnel City Group. The next layer up is the Jordan Sandstone, lying under a dolomite cap of the Prairie du Chien Group. The sandstones were all deposited in the late Cambrian Period, around 500 million years ago. Cross-bedding in some layers indicates that sand dunes once lay in this area, first molded by wind and later by the shallow water of an advancing sea. The presence of the greenish clay mineral glauconite in the Tunnel City sandstone tells of the Cambrian sea deepening over the area and depositing finer sediments. The dolomite cap was deposited by a later sea early in the Ordovician Period.

The nearly vertical faces of these bluffs were eroded by glacial meltwaters that filled the river valley 10,000 years ago. Here the river rounds a bend, flowing west then southwest, with the bluffs sitting on its northwest bank. The glacial floodwaters flowed much higher than today's river, wearing away at the bluffs for centuries, washing eroded sandstone downstream and undercutting the dolomite caps.

Ferry Bluff is named for a Civil War–era ferry service operated by the Laws brothers, Moses and Persis, who used a rowboat to tow a flatbed ferry back and forth across the river. They carried mostly farmers and their livestock between the base of the bluff and the flat floodplain across the river. The passengers reached the bluff side of the river using the same 1-mile route that visitors use today: Ferry Bluff Road. It begins at WI 60, about 4 miles east of Sauk City, and ends at a parking area and trailhead. The trail angles up the draw between the two bluffs and circles back toward the river to the top of Cactus Bluff, where visitors will find a set of signs informing them of the geology, biology, and fragility of this protected state natural area. An unmarked trail goes northeast to the undeveloped top of Ferry Bluff.

On the dry south-facing slopes of these and other river bluffs are remnants of dry prairie, and hikers often see prickly pear cactus on the bluff tops. The bluffs are closed to hikers between November 15 and March 31 every year because bald eagles and other raptors roost here in winter, including the rare peregrine falcon in years past.

Dolomite (top) caps Jordan Sandstone on Cactus Bluff. Note the cross-bedding in the sandstone.

View looking southwest at the Wisconsin River valley from atop Cactus Bluff.

52 UNIVERSITY OF WISCONSIN GEOLOGY MUSEUM

Rocks, Minerals, Fossils, and Much More

On the south side of the University of Wisconsin–Madison campus is Weeks Hall, home of the Department of Geosciences and the UW Geology Museum. Now in its eighteenth decade, the museum houses colorful, well-crafted exhibits that offer a complete introduction to geology and paleontology for beginners, as well as much more detailed information for those with some knowledge of these fields. The exhibits include displays on plate tectonics, rocks and minerals, fossils, caves, glaciers, dinosaurs, geologic time, and a rotating model of Earth, 6 feet in diameter.

The museum got its start in 1848 when Madison newspaperman Horace A. Tenney put out a call to communities all over the state asking for contributions of artifacts to be collected in a geology museum. This statewide public project continues today, with additions to its collection sent from people around the state. Museum Director Richard Slaughter, who puts a high priority on continuing that tradition, says, "I love to tell the kids, 'This is our collection. All of us in Wisconsin own it.'"

Today, the museum houses items from all over the world, including a beautiful collection of rocks and minerals with information on what they are and how they were formed. Equally impressive is the fossil collection, which includes striking displays of crinoids (sea lilies), various corals, primitive fish, stem reptiles (thought to be the ancestors of dinosaurs

A bed of crinoid (sea lily) fossils, collected by a UW geology student.

An ichnofossil showing 4-to-5-inch-wide tracks of sluglike Climactichnites.

and all modern reptiles), birds, and mammals. Also on display are superb examples of ichnofossils—not bones, but traces left behind by ancient creatures, such as the tracks of sluglike *Climactichnites*, ancient jellyfish impressions, and the tiny tracks of scampering primitive crab-like crustaceans. Unique items on display include a piece of the oldest known rock on Earth—4.4 billion years old—from Australia; fossils of stromatolites, one of the oldest known forms of life; and part of the meteorite that formed Meteor Crater in Arizona, the first crater on Earth recognized to have formed from a meteor impact.

One of the most popular exhibits is the set of massive skeletons—a large plant-eating duck-billed dinosaur called *Edmontosaurus*, the skull of a *Tyrannosaurus rex*, and an American mastodon, an elephant-like mammal that lived during the ice ages. The latter, called the Boaz Mastodon, is constructed from fossils found at two sites in Richland County, part of the Driftless Area, in the 1890s. Four brothers found huge bones emerging from a creek bed on their family farm near Boaz after a heavy rainstorm. Researchers also found a fluted, quartzite spear point near the bones, which indicated that humans might have killed the animal. Archeologists used this find to establish that humans lived in the unglaciated Driftless Area during glacial times. The Boaz Mastodon, living about 12,150 years ago, was 9.5 feet tall and 15 feet long and weighed around 8 tons. The other mastodon was discovered near Boaz in the village of Anderson Mills. It lived around 12,900 years ago.

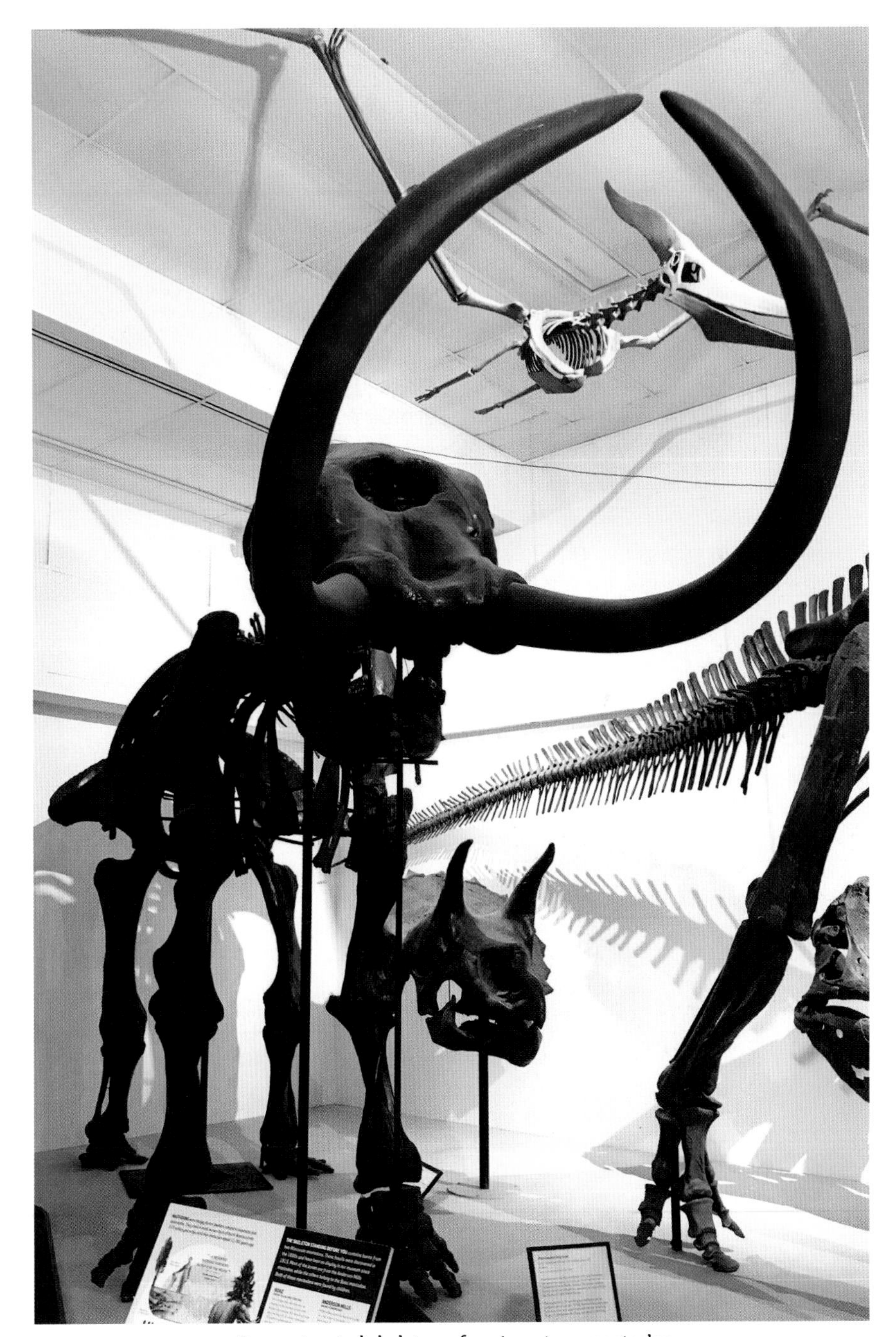

Reconstructed skeleton of an American mastodon.

On display at the UW Geology Museum is part of the meteorite that formed a famous crater in Arizona.

A sample of the minerals on display at the UW Geology Museum.

GLOSSARY

almandine. A variety of garnet, deep red to brownish red, found in igneous and metamorphic rocks.

amphibole. A group of iron- and magnesium-bearing silicate minerals commonly found in igneous and metamorphic rocks. Includes the mineral hornblende.

amphibolite. A type of rock formed by metamorphism of basalt or gabbro under medium to high temperatures and pressures. It consists largely of the minerals amphibole and plagioclase.

andesite. A fine-grained, crystalline extrusive rock of volcanic origin with an intermediate silica composition between basalt and rhyolite; the extrusive equivalent of diorite.

basalt. A brown to black extrusive igneous rock made of tiny crystals that form when lava cools quickly. It is composed largely of calcium-rich feldspar and dark minerals such as pyroxene and olivine; the extrusive equivalent of gabbro.

batholith. A large region of igneous rock, usually greater than 40 square miles.

biotite. A black, brown, or dark-green mineral of the mica group.

brachiopods. A class of invertebrates having a bivalve shell that is bilaterally symmetrical.

braided stream. A broad, shallow stream flowing within many interconnected and shifting channels.

breccia. A rock made of angular fragments cemented together to form a mass. Fault breccia is created by the fracturing and crushing of rock along a fault.

bryozoans. A phylum of invertebrate colonial marine animals.

calcareous. Containing calcium carbonate ($CaCO_3$).

calcite. The mineral form of calcium carbonate ($CaCO_3$).

Canadian Shield. The ancient bedrock core of North America. It underlies most of central and eastern Canada and the northern parts of Minnesota, Wisconsin, and New York.

case hardening. A process in which sandstone is hardened on its surface by a cement or crust created by the evaporation of mineral-bearing solutions.

cephalopod. A class of mollusks with a prominent head, bilateral symmetry, and tentacles; for example, an octopus.

chert. A dense, hard, fine-grained rock made entirely of silica. In Wisconsin most chert formed by the infusion of silica-rich fluids flowing over and through dolomite. Variously colored gray, black, brown, orange, yellowish, reddish, and green. Also called *flint*.

cleavage. Tendency of a mineral or rock to split along closely spaced planes.

coarse-grained. A term used to describe a rock with large particles or crystals usually visible to the naked eye.

conglomerate. A type of rock made of sand and rounded pebbles, cobbles, and/or boulders, cemented together.

cross-bedding. Layers in sedimentary rocks that form at an angle to horizontal and are often deposited by flowing water or wind currents.

cross fault. A short fault that lies at an angle to a larger fault.

cuesta. An asymmetrical ridge with a steep side, called an escarpment, and a gently sloping side.

dalles. A stretch of a stream channel or river gorge with steep sides; from the French word *dale*, which means "slab." Dalles are typically made of layers of rock resembling slabs.

differential erosion. The variation in rates of erosion between adjacent rock types.

diorite. A coarse-grained intrusive igneous rock intermediate in composition between granite and gabbro; the intrusive equivalent of andesite.

dolomite. A type of rock made from limestone by the replacement of some or all of the calcium carbonate by magnesium carbonate. The technical name for this rock is *dolomitic limestone* or *dolostone*.

Driftless Area. The area of southwestern Wisconsin, along with smaller adjacent areas of Minnesota, Iowa, and Illinois, that was never covered by glacial ice.

dripstone. See *speleothem*.

escarpment. The steep side of a ridge or plateau.

esker. A narrow, often sinuous ridge made of sand and gravel deposited by glacial meltwater within a tunnel under a glacier.

extrusive rock. Rock that cools from lava at the surface of the Earth.

fault. A fracture in bedrock across which the sections of rock are differentially displaced.

Favosites. A genus of extinct Paleozoic corals whose fossils resemble honeycombs; also called honeycomb corals.

feldspar. The most abundant group of rock-forming minerals, including potassium-bearing, or alkali, feldspars (orthoclase) and calcium- and sodium-bearing feldspars (plagioclase). Common in igneous and metamorphic rocks and sediments eroded from them.

fine-grained. A term used to describe a rock with small particles or crystals typically not visible to the naked eye.

formation. A body of rock that can be recognized and mapped over a large area. A formation may be part of a larger group or may be divided into members.

gabbro. A dark-colored, coarse-grained, intrusive igneous rock composed mostly of calcium plagioclase feldspar and pyroxene; the intrusive equivalent of basalt.

galena. A lead sulfide mineral that is an important ore of lead.

glacial erratic. A boulder carried from one location to another by a glacier.

glacial lake. A body of water formed from melting glacial ice dammed on one or more sides by retreating walls of ice. It can exist for many decades or centuries and drains away when the glacier melts.

glacial till. The material collected, moved, and dropped in a new location by a glacier; includes silt, sand, gravel, and boulders.

glaciation. A major southerly advance of a continental ice sheet. Wisconsin experienced several during the Pleistocene ice ages.

glacier. A mass of ice formed from compacted and recrystallized snow that expands and flows across a land area and persists over long periods of time. It is moved by the internal pressure of the growing mass and by gravity on downsloping land. When covering a large region, it is called an *ice sheet*. Bulging areas of an ice sheet are called *lobes*.

glauconite. A greenish clay mineral formed by the alteration of clay or mica minerals on relatively undisturbed areas of a seafloor.

gneiss. A coarse-grained rock formed by the metamorphism of granite or other igneous rock; usually banded, with darker minerals alternating with lighter minerals.

granite. A coarse-grained, light-colored, intrusive igneous rock composed primarily of quartz and potassium feldspar.

greenstone. Metamorphosed igneous rock colored green by the presence of chlorite or epidote.

Halysites. A genus of extinct Paleozoic corals whose fossils resemble fragile chains; also called chain corals.

hummocky terrain. Terrain made up of randomly arranged hills, ridges, hollows, ravines, and kettles created by the collapse of debris lying on top of and contained within a glacier as the ice melts away.

hyolithid. An extinct invertebrate, most commonly from the Cambrian Period, having a limey univalve shell.

ice-walled lake plain. A flat-topped hill, the top of which was once a lake bottom on top of a glacier. Glacial debris collected on the bottom of the lake, and when the ice walls of the lake melted, the debris slumped onto the land to form a hill.

ichnofossil. A trace, such as a track or body part impression, left behind by an ancient creature.

igneous rock. Rock that solidified from the cooling of magma or lava.

interlobate zone. The zone where the margins of two glacial lobes meet to form a long, often doubly large moraine.

intrusive rock. Rock that cools from magma beneath the surface of the Earth. The body of rock is called an intrusion.

iron oxide. A red, crystalline, water-insoluble solid occurring commonly as rust.

joint. A fracture that traverses a body of rock, often occurring in sets, along which no appreciable movement of rock has occurred.

kame. A conical hill formed of glacial debris deposited by a stream that flowed vertically through a shaft, called a *moulin*, from the surface of the glacier to its base. Also called *moulin kame*.

kaolinite. A common aluminum silicate clay mineral found in sediments, soils, and sedimentary rock.

karst. A type of bedrock laced with crevices, caves, and sinkholes created by the chemical erosion of carbonate rock by slightly acidic groundwater.

kettle. A generally pot-shaped depression in Earth's surface formed after a block of stagnant glacial ice, trapped under glacial debris, melted.

Keweenawan. See *Midcontinent Rift*.

limonite. A commonly occurring iron oxide of variable composition.

loess. Glacial silt blown and deposited by wind. It was usually picked up by the wind from recently deglaciated outwash plains that had dried. It forms a component of some of Wisconsin's rich soils.

magma. Molten rock.

magnetite. A black strongly magnetic iron mineral that is an important ore of iron.

metamorphic rock. Rock derived from preexisting rock that changed in response to elevated temperatures and pressure. The change, or recrystallization, is call *metamorphism*.

mica. A group of silicate minerals with a sheetlike structure; they separate readily into thin, tough, often transparent and bendable sheets.

Midcontinent Rift. An area of the North American crust where a plume of magma rose from the mantle 1.1 billion years ago and fractured the crust in an arcing pattern running from Kansas northeast to Lake Superior, east along the length of the lake's basin, and then southeast into Michigan. It threatened to split the continent in two until it stopped for some as yet undetermined reason. Also known as the *Keweenawan episode*.

moraine. A long ridge of glacial debris (sand, gravel, and boulders) that formed at the margin of the glacier over a long period of time.

moulin. A vertical shaft running from the surface of a glacier to its base.

moulin kame. See *kame*.

orogeny. A mountain building event or process involving faulting and folding.

outwash. Glacial debris (sand, rocks, and boulders) deposited by braided streams flowing away from a glacial margin.

oxidation. A weathering process by which elements on the surface of a rock combine with oxygen in the atmosphere.

plagioclase. A feldspar mineral rich in calcium and sodium; a common mineral in igneous and metamorphic rocks.

plate tectonics. The shifting of Earth's crustal plates atop the underlying hot, plastic mantle. Areas where plates meet and interact are common sites for earthquakes, volcanic eruptions, and mountain building.

pothole. A pot-shaped hole drilled into bedrock by grindstones caught in strong eddies over long periods of time; commonly formed in glacial meltwater streams.

quartz. Silicon dioxide (SiO_2), a colorless or tinted, transparent rock-forming mineral. Quartz is the most abundant and widespread of all minerals and a major component of most sands, sandstones, and quartzite.

quartzite. A metamorphic rock made mostly of quartz sandstone metamorphosed by pressure and/or heat and cemented by silica; an extremely hard and resistant rock.

rhyolite. Reddish, fine-grained extrusive igneous rock containing quartz and potassium feldspar in the same proportions as granite.

rift. A long narrow trough in a continent that has undergone extensional stresses. Lava extrudes at the surface, and sediments collect in the low-lying region.

sandstone. A sedimentary rock composed primarily of sand grains cemented together, over long periods of time, by the pressure of burial and by various substances, including silica, iron oxide, calcium carbonate, and clay.

saprolite. A soft decomposed igneous or metamorphic rock rich in clay minerals, especially kaolinite, formed in place by chemical weathering.

schist. A coarse-grained metamorphic rock that splits easily into thin plates or slabs.

sedimentary rock. A rock formed by the compaction and cementation of sediments.

shale. A fine-grained sedimentary rock formed from mud or soft clay minerals.

silica. The compound silicon dioxide (SiO_2).

siltstone. A rock formed from silt having shale-like texture and composition.

Skolithos. A genus of ichnofossils that are vertical tubes where worms burrowed into the sandy bottoms of shallow shorelines.

solution features. Bedrock features, including caves, crevices, and sinkholes, formed by the erosive action of slightly acidic groundwater.

speleothem. A cave feature, including stalactites, stalagmites, columns, and flowstone, resulting from the deposition of minerals by water inside a cave.

stream capture. A process wherein a stream breaks through some barrier and takes a new course of least resistance, abandoning its former route.

striations. Scratches on bedrock outcroppings made by hard stones embedded in the bottom of an advancing glacier.

stromatoporoids. A class of extinct colonial organisms whose fossils resemble sponges.

subduction. A process wherein one of two converging tectonic plates dives beneath the other. The leading edge of the subducting (diving) plate gets mangled and broken apart, and some of its rock sinks into the mantle where it melts and creates new magma.

subsidence. The sinking of a section of land.

syenite. A coarse-grained igneous rock composed largely of alkali feldspar. It resembles granite but lacks quartz.

syncline. A downward fold in the crust resembling a trough.

Syringopora. A genus of extinct corals whose fossils resemble tubes.

talus. An accumulation of fragmented rock, typically piled along the base of a cliff or bluff.

tannin. An astringent organic compound derived from plants.

terrace. An erosional remnant of a former floodplain standing above the modern stream.

till. See *glacial till*.

topographic reversal. A process wherein high points on the land become low points, and vice versa. In glacial terrain, a thin layer of debris covering a high point on the glacier becomes a low point when the glacier melts, whereas thick debris filling a low point on the glacier becomes a hill.

trilobite. Any of several extinct arthropods with external skeletons and several appendages for movement.

tunnel channel. The bed of a subglacial stream of meltwater, varying greatly in length, width, and depth. Its size is indicative of how fast the meltwater flowed beneath the glacier.

vesicle. Space in a body of lava rock where gases or minerals less dense than the lava rose to the surface of the lava flow and were trapped as the lava cooled. A layer of vesicles marks the top of a lava flow.

Wisconsin Dome. The area of north-central Wisconsin that was gently heaved up to create a highland between the two extensions of the Midcontinent Rift. It is up to 600 feet higher than areas to the west, south, and east.

Wisconsin glaciation. The most recent glaciation, so named because Wisconsin showcases many of its features, as well as unglaciated land.

FURTHER READING

GENERAL SOURCES

Attig, John W., Lee Clayton, Kenneth I. Lange, and Louis J. Maher. 1990. *The Ice Age Geology of Devils Lake State Park.* Educational Series 35. Wisconsin Geological and Natural History Survey.

Austin, Joel D. 2014. *Discovering the Penokees*. Gaylord, MI: Sweetwater Visions.

Bell, Jeannette, and Chet Bell. 2000. *County Parks of Wisconsin: 600 Parks You Can Visit Featuring 25 Favorites*. Madison, WI: Trails Books.

Dott, Robert H., Jr., and John W. Attig. 2004. *Roadside Geology of Wisconsin*. Missoula, MT: Mountain Press Publishing Company.

Eaton, Conan Bryant. 2002. *Rock Island: A Part of the History of Washington Township*. Washington Island, WI: Jackson Harbor Press.

LaBerge, Gene L. 1994. *Geology of the Lake Superior Region*. Tucson, AZ: Geoscience Press.

Martin, Lawrence. 1965. *The Physical Geography of Wisconsin*. Madison: University of Wisconsin Press.

Mickelson, David M., Louis J. Maher, Jr., and Susan L. Simpson. 2011. *Geology of the Ice Age National Scenic Trail*. Madison: University of Wisconsin Press.

Paull, Rachel K., and Richard A. Paull. 1980. *Wisconsin and Upper Michigan: Including Parts of Adjacent States*. Dubuque, IA: Kendall/Hunt Publishing Company.

Peterson, Ryan, and William S. Cordua. 2013. *Geology Walking Tour, Wisconsin Interstate Park of St. Croix Falls, Polk County, WI*. River Falls: Wisconsin Department of Natural Resources and UW—River Falls.

Pond, Alonzo W. 1937. *Interstate Park and Dalles of the St. Croix*. St. Croix Falls: The Standard-Press.

Schultz, Gwen. 2004. *Wisconsin's Foundations: A Review of the State's Geology and Its Influence on Geography and Human Activity*. Madison: University of Wisconsin Press.

Tishler, William H. 2006. *Door County's Emerald Treasure: A History of Peninsula State Park*. Madison: University of Wisconsin Press.

TECHNICAL SOURCES

Bedrock Stratigraphic Units of Wisconsin. 2011. Wisconsin Geological and Natural History Survey, Educational Series 51.

Brzeskiewicz, M. E. 2014. *Establishment Record for St. Peters Dome Research Natural Area*. US Department of Agriculture Forest Service, Chequamegon-Nicolet National Forest.

Clayton, Lee, and John W. Attig. 1990. *Geology of Sauk County, Wisconsin*. Wisconsin Geological and Natural History Survey, Information Circular No. 67.

Cleland, Herdman F. 1911. *The Fossils and Stratigraphy of the Middle Devonian of Wisconsin.* Wisconsin Geological and Natural History Survey, Bulletin 21, Scientific Series No. 6.

Cole, H. E. 1918. *A Standard History of Sauk County Wisconsin*. Chicago: Lewis Publishing Company.

Crawford, D. 2009. *Geology of Interstate Park: The St. Croix Dalles*. Pamphlet. Minnesota Department of Natural Resources.

Cummings, M. L., and J. V. Scrivner. 1980. "The Saprolite at the Precambrian-Cambrian Contact, Irvine Park, Chippewa Falls, Wisconsin." *Transactions of the Wisconsin Academy of Sciences, Arts, and Letters* 68: 22–29.

Dalziel, I. W. D., and Robert H. Dott, Jr. 1970. *Geology of the Baraboo District, Wisconsin*. Wisconsin Geological and Natural History Survey, Information Circular No. 14.

Davies, W. E., and I. M. Morgan. 1980. *Geology of Caves*. US Department of Interior/Geological Survey.

Day, M. J. 2017. *Sandstone Caves in Wisconsin*. Prairie du Sac, WI: Wisconsin Speleological Society.

Day, M. J. 2008. "A Speleogenic Origin for the Leland Natural Bridge, Wisconsin?" *Wisconsin Geographer* 23: 50–66.

Dictionary of Geology and Mineralogy. 2nd ed. 2003. New York: McGraw-Hill.

Dott, Robert H., Jr., and Roger L. Batten. 1988. *Evolution of the Earth.* 4th ed. New York: McGraw-Hill.

Kluessendorf, Joanne, and Donald G. Mikulic. 2004. *The Lake and the Ledge: Geological Links between the Niagara Escarpment and Lake Winnebago.* 65th Annual Tri-State Geological Field Conference. Menasha: Weis Earth Science Museum, University of Wisconsin—Fox Valley.

LaBerge, Gene L., and Paul E. Myers. 1983. *Precambrian Geology of Marathon County, Wisconsin.* Wisconsin Geological and Natural History Survey, Information Circular No. 45.

Luczaj, John A. 2010. "Fonferek Glen County Park," In *Great Lakes SEPM/Tri-State Geological Conference Field Trip Guidebook.* Champaign, IL: Illinois State Geological Survey.

Luczaj, John A. 2013. "Geology of the Niagara Escarpment in Wisconsin." *Geoscience Wisconsin* 22, Part 1. Published online. Wisconsin Geological and Natural History Survey.

Luczaj, John A. 2000. *Preliminary Geologic Map of the Buried Bedrock Surface, Brown County, Wisconsin*. Wisconsin Geological and Natural History Survey.

Luczaj, John A. 2017. "Ship Rock Wayside." In *73rd Annual Great Lakes SEPM/Tri-State Geological Conference Field Trip Guidebook*. Menasha: University of Wisconsin–Fox Valley.

Maass, R. S. 1986. *Penokean Deformation and Metamorphism in Central Wisconsin: Volcanic Rocks and Gneisses.* Field Trip Guidebook Prepared for 32nd Annual Meeting Institute on Lake Superior Geology, Wisconsin Rapids, Apr. 28–May 4, 1986. Wisconsin Geological and Natural History Survey.

Meyers, P. E., M. L. Cummings, and S. L. Wurdinger. 1980. *Precambrian Geology of the Chippewa Valley, Field Guide.* Prepared for the 26th Annual Institute on Lake Superior Geology. University of Wisconsin–Eau Claire.

Paull, Richard A. 1992. "First Report of Natural Bridges in Eastern Wisconsin." *Transactions of the Wisconsin Academy of Sciences, Arts, and Letters* 80: 139–48.

Stieglitz, Ronald D. 2016. "Introduction to Wisconsin's Niagara Escarpment." *Geoscience Wisconsin* 22, Introduction. Published online. Wisconsin Geological and Natural History Survey.

Thwaites, F. T. 1961. "The Base of the St. Peter Sandstone in Southwestern Wisconsin." *Wisconsin Academy of Sciences, Arts, and Letters* 50: 203–19.

Travis, Jack W. 2009. *Field Trip Guide Book: Geology of Brown and Door Counties, Wisconsin*. 2009 Spring Meeting of the Wisconsin Section of the American Institute of Professional Geologists.

INDEX

Born and raised in northern Wisconsin, **SCOTT SPOOLMAN** has long been fascinated with his native state's forests, waters, and rocks. His early experiences fed into a long career as a science writer. He obtained a master's degree in science journalism from the University of Minnesota and then worked for textbook publishing companies, including a stint as geology editor for McGraw-Hill, before starting a freelance writing business. He and his wife, Gail, who now live in Madison, raised two children, and as a family they explored the natural areas of Wisconsin and neighboring states.